# Mortime
# Goes N

## by Tim Stafford

Illustrations by Kate Simpson

Published in Great Britain in 2013 by Powdene Publicity Ltd,
Unit 17, Quay Level, St. Peter's Wharf, Newcastle upon Tyne, NE6 1TZ
© Tim Stafford, 2013. All rights reserved.
email:durhamtim@hotmail.com
A catalogue record for this book is available from the British Library.
ISBN: 978-0-9926969-1-7
Printed by Pennyprint, Tyne and Wear

Tim Stafford is retired. He spent the first few years of his life in Africa where he learnt Swahili and how to run wild. He was educated, after a fashion, in the South of England where he also began his career as a land agent eventually moving to Northumberland to work for The National Trust.
He is married to the long suffering Sid and has two sons and five grand-children.
His great passions, other than his family, are dogs, horses, fishing, parties and everything outside.

## DEDICATED TO

Pooh (AKA Sid), Nick and Jamie

### Very many thanks to

Pooh for struggling through His early texts thereby having to relive all those horrors while correcting His smelling pistakes.

Margaret Clow who had to decipher what He calls handwriting.

Stewart Bonney of Powdene for being brave enough to publish His ramblings with a smile.

Katie Simpson for the lovely illustrations.

### NB

Once again, suing Him would be pointless as it really has all gone on horses, helicopters and whisky.

# Foreword

He named me Worm for no obvious reason. A pretty bizarre name but marginally better than those He chose for my siblings. I shared my eccentric home with my Mother, Mortimer Fish (MF), and my two brothers Maggot and Grub. There you are you see. In due course they went off to new and probably more ordered establishments leaving me and MF with Him. I have taken up the pen to record the next stage of our lives while my Mother has retired into a comfortable and self-indulgent old age.

All childhoods are a steep learning curve and none more so than mine. By nature I am more fiery than my Mother and as He gets older He gets less predictable and steadily more and more barmy. Nonetheless once I had learnt how to view our relationships we shook down into some sort of chaotic rhythm. However nothing much prepares one for the hurly burly of life with Him.

For the first few years we shared His tatty house in a small Dorset village. His wife had died so inevitably from time to time an unsuitably young girlfriend would be in evidence along with His stepchildren who blew in for sleep and refreshment. Coming from an agricultural background He spent a lot of His time pursuing predictable hobbies like fishing and hunting. Less expected though was His passion for flying a thoroughly dangerous two-seater helicopter. Occasionally He did some work. He took us on long and enjoyable walks on the estate and in the New Forest nearby. My mother and Uncle introduced me to the delights of ratting and rabbiting.

His horses lived in stables adjacent to the house and, in theory, that was where His groom, the Lovely Kate, did her work but she spent a lot of her time in the domestic quarters trying to civilise Him and us. She was becoming expert at patching up both Him and the horses when they returned from hunting.

The domestic chaos inside the house was sorted out by the long suffering Heather. She would arrive from her home in a neighbouring village, view the mess with a good natured resignation and begin the task of mucking it out all over again and navigating the now ageing Dyson round the accumulating junk.

After a few years He decided to move back to the family farm in Northumberland. That move alone was a logistical nightmare and the cause of a good many parties and disasters. There His ex-wife, Sid (She-in-Doors), took Him back which everyone considered either foolhardy or saint-like. Most of us reckon that she must enjoy a challenge.

MF wrote an account of her first few years in her book The Journal of Mortimer Fish. What follows is the next few years. Not much has changed. Once in Northumberland We shared the house with Sid's two dogs Brain Dead and Nearly Dead. There is also an unbelievably old cat who used to belong to His Mother.

# My Diary

Today was not very funny. I was not keen to get into the car with Him. He had a purposeful look about Him which is pretty unusual in one who appears to achieve so little. What's more we left MF at home which is almost unheard of. He doesn't reckon that the car is properly furnished without her. Anyhow we went to the vet in Blandford. This was my first visit to this place and I didn't know what to expect. It had a strong canine smell mingled with cat and I was immediately on my guard. There were quite a lot of other dogs in the waiting area and one or two cats in baskets. He put me on a lead so that I couldn't have a go at anything or anyone. This was a bit unsporting of Him so I grumbled at just about everything. Other dogs on leads just irritate me. The fact that I am attached to one just compounds the problem. Eventually we went into a small room and someone dressed in white overalls like an angel without the wing attachments took my temperature in a most unseemly way; so I bit her. They put a muzzle on me then so I had a go at that too but no matter how hard you try it won't get bit. Anyhow He left me there. Well I may not be quite as besotted with Him as MF is but I thought that it was an unfriendly act and I would have told Him so if He hadn't left so quickly. The silly grin should have warned me.

## June 21st

He came to fetch me at lunch time and I probably overdid the enthusiasm bit but I was really glad to see Him. Kate's sister Sarah who is a vet nurse there looked after me while I was in the ghastly place and I have rather taken to her. She's not as glamorous as Kate but has a nice way with me. She seemed genuinely concerned about my little operation which He sarcastically refers to as my "major surgical procedure" so I didn't bite her.

I am very sore in an intimate place and to be honest doing my usual "pleased to see you" wiggle is not to be recommended. That is all I'm going to say on the subject. I was glad to get back to the asylum. Piglet just laughed in an oafish way. MF was smug having had Him all to herself for twenty-four hours.

## July 2nd

I have quite recovered from my visit to Blandford. We went for a goodish walk in Little Wood today with Kate, MF, Him and oafish Uncle Piglet. June and Susan have fenced off part of the park with natty looking orange sheep netting. This contains some lambs that looked eminently chaseable. In order to get to the lambs one has to negotiate the orange netting. Well no one had explained that it was electrified. I went for it with a will and I got stuck in it. God knows how many volts were pulsating round my body but it made me yell a good deal. It was quite gratifying to see how quickly He came to my rescue. Kate just laughed. It is a cruel world. I am suddenly profoundly cynical about female humans who can find being electrocuted amusing. I am not impressed.

I didn't get much sympathy from MF or Piglet either. They were too busy charging about looking for the rabbit we all know lives under Rose Princes cottage.

## November 4th

He got back from hunting rather early today all crippled up. At least the horse is okay. Kate wasn't too unsympathetic but laughed a good deal at the grass skid marks on His hunting coat. She seems amused at other people's misfortune.

It seems He came off at the gallop in a flat field nowhere near the action. He was badly winded and people thought He was dying. There was already an ambulance nearby scraping someone else off the field who was suspected of having had a heart attack. His friends suggested putting Him in the same blood wagon but He declined claiming that too few people come out of hospital vertical.

Anyhow the beautiful Sarah Kate, another absurdly pretty girl who did untold damage to His blood pressure, put Him back on His horse and off He went again. Then His chest began to hurt rather a lot. He couldn't even last until the end of a promising story from Julian Gordon Watson before He had to excuse Himself and hack back to His lorry at Throope.

## November 7th

He went to see His doctor today. It seems that He has cracked a couple of ribs on the left hand side. His long suffering doctor Liz has given Him some strong pain killers. What is most important she has allowed Him to continue His daily intake of whisky.

## December 18th

He's in serious trouble with Kate. He and I went out on an exercise ride across the Estate. Him on Spider and me following. We got back to the yard a couple of hours later Him leading the brute. He was only supposed to be away an hour. It was His first ride for a long time so it was expected that He would take a bit of care.

Anyhow, while trying to ride the horse through a hedge at the furthest end of the estate– and one is bound to ask why would anyone try to ride through a hedge – He got hung up half garrotted, by a branch. The brute, Spider, then bolted and dumped Him onto a big flint. He, not wishing to lose the beast, a couple of miles from home, held on to the reins so that when Spider reared up He very nearly dislocated both His shoulders. He let the horse go and watched it gallop away towards home. This particular farm is arable and has no fences or gates so He was in a fever of anxiety about Spider getting onto the road.

At that moment a military helicopter came over very low. It is hard to credit that He really did try to hail it in the hope of getting a lift to chase and catch the animal. Spider is frightened of cars and tractors so the mind boggles at what he'd do if a helicopter came any where near him. Needless to say the machine didn't stop for Him. Eventually we did catch up with Spider but He couldn't get back on because of the pain in His shoulders and a searing pain in His bottom. What He had failed to notice was that Spider too was injured. Kate had no sympathy for Him. He slunk back in to the house leaving Spider to be patched up with the help of another expensive visit from Bob the horse vet from Salisbury.

He took us for a walk but it was a rather slow tedious affair and He seemed a bit out of sorts.

## January 8th

He is grounded for the nonce because of the shoulder injuries and a sore bottom. Spider is off games too so He took us hunting on foot. We didn't get the luxury of a lead. We were attached to Him by long bits of orange bailer twine which I thought was a bit undignified. We were in the Chalke valley which meant some long treks up and down the lovely turf hills.

He met an old friend and the gossiping began. Fish hates being attached to Him like this and the chatting was pretty boring. Piglet and I sat down at their feet quite content to doze but unknown to Him Fish began to chew her way through the string. Eventually she escaped without Him noticing. She legged it towards a good thick hedge which separated the followers from the hounds who were drawing a covert on the other side. Suddenly there was an angry roar from the covert. Amongst the recognisable words however was something to the effect that could someone remove the blank, blanking terrier from the pack. The penny dropped. He was galvanised into activity. We went tearing off as fast as His sore bits would let Him. Yell as He would MF failed to respond. Presumably she was having the time of her life with the hounds and the rancid smell of fox all over the place. The Master continued to give tongue. As there was nothing He could do to retrieve " The Terrier" He waited for the hounds to move on which they did eventually. MF returned looking ridiculously pleased with herself. He was amazingly unmoved by it all. He didn't even admonish MF.

## January 21st

His injuries are abating. After our uneventful morning walk to Little Wood and back He had arranged to borrow Karen's horse which is a lot smaller than Spider. This was His first serious exercise ride since His accident in December. We all went into the yard to watch this momentous occasion. Kate was already on Spider so He climbed up the very rickety wooden mounting block. As He poised himself to get on board the mounting block collapsed under Him propelling Him onto the point of His left shoulder on the ground where He lay blaspheming. Kate told Him to catch the horse which was about to abscond. He is not given to getting cross and very rarely swears. This time He did both. This quietened Kate a good deal and He hobbled back into the house.

We had never heard Him yell at Kate before so it was quite a shock and probably to her too. She went very silent. Anyhow the upshot is that His reintroduction to the hunting field has been delayed for a little longer. That suits us as we get rather better walks.

## February 10th

John the farmer has been putting rat poison round the pheasant feeders up in the park. Me and Piglet go ratting up and down the overgrown hedges on our walks and we usually manage to flush out a few to chase. Now and then we catch one. Piglet gets one end and I get the other and we pull until the bits separate. Sometimes we have to share bits with MF. We then have the joy of taking our trophy to Him or Kate. Rats are not nice to eat but we inevitably ingest bits. The poison is a sort of bright green colour. We didn't know it was poison of course. After that we went on into Little Wood and Piglet chased just about anything that moved. That scared Him in case He lost Piglet and had to face Kate. Anyhow just as we got near Keepers Cottage a sporting rabbit got up and ran off with the three of us in pursuit. Manic Piglet doesn't really look where he is going and led us through a barbed wire fence. I caught my ear on it and left quite a chunk of my left lobe on a barb. I yelled a lot and He came running over. It was quite gratifying how concerned He was. He retrieved the bit of ear and tried to console me. I'm a bit worried about that bit of ear. He has a warped sense of humour. Is it going to be sewn back on or is it a trophy to be added to the jar on the mantle-piece containing those bits of uncle Piglet referred to in MF's book.

We got back to the house and my ear hurt and stung rather a lot. I shook my head to try to alleviate the pain. The ear was still bleeding badly so that all I achieved was a new method of mass decoration. I completely covered the kitchen with tasteful little red dots. I'm quite touchy about my body and wouldn't let Him near me so the bleeding went on. I'm not sure it bothered Him too much. At first He laughed then the thought of what Heather might say made Him scurry round trying to clean up after me.

This afternoon He and Kate found bright green "you knows" on the lawn. Quite obviously contaminated with rat poison. It was quite pleasing the way they worried. The upshot is that Piglet and I were bundled into the car and taken to the vets where they pronounced us both hale and hearty but they took blood samples.

*Me and MF*

**February 14th**

He went hunting with the Wilton again today and returned positively pulsating with adrenalin. He was full of tales of galloping and jumping round Mary Gordon Watson's old cross country course near Cranborne. And how He had jumped a barbed wire fence to get back to the lorry. Then the bombshell struck. Kate told Him that she reckoned poor Spider had done his check ligament again. " He's very lame and how come you didn't notice it....?" It seems that many years ago in Northumberland He team chased a lame horse without either He or the horse noticing!

**February 16th**

The laboratory results for our blood samples are back. It seems that we have been affected by the rat poison but not enough to worry about. Poor John got it in the neck for distributing it and He gets very agitated when we go anywhere near the feeders. What's more He takes a disproportionately greater interest in our bowel movements now. It's all becoming a bit too personal.

Bob the horse vet came today passing through so to speak. After endless expensive scans and so on Bob says that Spider will never hunt again. Give Him His due, He is desolate. However He must have a financial death wish because He's decided to buy another horse.

**February 18th.**

So today He took us to a meet of the Portman Hunt at a girlfriend's farm. It was a beautiful, warm day. Once again He was on foot and as usual we were on bits of bailer twine. He watched, mesmerised, as an extremely pretty girl riding a beautiful grey mare peeled off her pullover in the sunshine. He nearly blew a fuse. What's more it seems that the girl wanted to sell her horse. So He, not needing much encouragement, sailed up to her and enquired about the animal. He asked her name and phone number (she looked mature enough to be able to parry that one). She replied "Lucy Ferry" and he responded (as He wrote it down) "as in North Sea?" We walked back to His friends who applauded Him for His downright ignorance. "Well who's this Bryan Ferry chap anyway?" He asked quite unabashed. We don't think He ever really understood why He had caused so much merriment. If the truth is known He would admit that as far as He was concerned all good pop music stopped when Elvis Presley died!

**April 8th**

Me and Piglet fell out today. He is, as I have said a good few times, oafish. Actually I blame the Lovely Kate. She sailed into the house just as He was getting MF and me our supper and Piglet who has the sensitivity of a door post scuttled into the pantry on his stumpy little legs and made straight for my food bowl. I went for him in a big way. Piglet played dirty by lying on his back with all his teeth out and made a blood curdling howl as if I had him by the jugular. Well Kate got all maternal and went for me with her welly. Fortunately He came to my rescue and after some pretty bad language from Piglet we separated but not before Kate had said some hurtful things about me. I think I have rather gone off her.

I used to argue with Grub, my brother, over food but I put that down to natural sibling rivalry but Piglet should know better.

**April 15th**

Grub, came to see us today. Not a good idea – we instantly argued over a toy on the lawn. I consider it pretty cheeky of him to march in as if he still lives here and claim the toy like that so the fur flew once more – quite like old times and I hate to admit it was rather fun. Anyhow I won. It seems that Grub and his new owner live in Farnham miles away. Grub has become urbane. He thinks he's sophisticated and has put on some airs and graces which don't sit comfortably in rural Dorset. I understand that they do have rats and squirrels but he gets to have a go at urban foxes now and then. I've never seen a rural one. He claims that He rarely sees one when He's hunting. Probably because He's usually looking down the neck of a flask. Anyhow He smiled a lot and got out drinks and pretended that it really didn't matter that 'Grub' had rocked our otherwise quite stable boat here. He's so predictable. My Mother just opens a weary eye, observes for a brief moment and goes back to sleep as if to say "I've seen it all before".

**May 10th**

There are some old abandoned Cambridge rollers beside one of the clumps of trees in the park. Piglet has decided that there is, or are rats snuggled up in there so he took to investigating just when He and Kate wanted to go home. To cut a long story short He got a bit hot under the collar and began to yell at Pig. That made it all the more clear that there was some truth in Pig's assertion so we all got stuck in. And sure enough there were two rats in residence. One shot out one end and the other, the other end. Despite Piglet being constructed like a small dirigible he can really move quite fast. His little legs go crazy, almost a blur, and off he went with me close behind. The poor thing didn't have a chance. We ended up at either end of the animal pulling away and eventually because pig is rather better anchored to the ground he won. In the meantime MF had chased her rat into the stump of an old tree where tear at the trunk as she might she simply couldn't get the tree to shift. In any case He hove into view, captured her with a lead and then He tried that on me but backed off when I showed Him both upper and lower sets. Piglet doesn't even like rat so capitulated more or less immediately. Kate is a bit girly about these things and left Him to toss what was left of the corpse into the tree so that we couldn't reach it. Spoil sports.

## June 3rd

He seems to go fishing more than ever. Usually we are left to wait in the deserted house. Today however He took us and it was not a good idea. It was all fairly new to me so the ritual was unfamiliar. I couldn't understand why MF and Piglet kept out of His way and went off rabbiting in the nettles. I found out. He was waving his rod about and all I could see was an annoying black insect apparently buzzing about my face so I snapped at it. It got caught in my upper lip. It was of course a fishing fly. He got cross and yelled a bit then He got concerned and tried to pull the fly out of my lip which was pretty silly really. I bit Him!

To be fair the fly didn't hurt so long as He didn't mess about with it. He cut the fishing line, packed up all His fishing paraphernalia and called to the other two. We all had to return to the car at the farm. We went back home where He decanted the hooligans and took me to the vet-again! I'm beginning not to like that smell. The wingless angel immediately put a muzzle on me, pricked me and waited till I was drifting off into rather a nice sleep. Then she removed the fly by cutting the shank. He was fairly grumpy about the fact that I had interrupted a day's fishing, cost Him an arm and a leg in vet bills and worst of all wasted a perfectly good fly.

I won't go fishing again unless forced to.

## July 12th

MF and I went for a hooley upstairs this morning. In Heather's absence on holiday He was attempting to do some ironing. What a pantomime He laid on for us. We sat in the entrance to the spare room overlooking the landing where He had set up the ironing board. He was tackling sheets. After a few goes at trying to work out how to put the whole sheet onto a narrow board all at once He decided to have a go at just one bit of it. As he went to work on that bit the rest of it slid off onto the floor on the far side. He went round the board tripped over the flex and landed up on the floor with it. He had another go at a different piece and the same thing happened. This time He got under the board and tried to feed the sheet back onto the board lying on His back. The sheet seemed determined not to be ironed and remained steadfastly crumpled on the floor. After a

*Me helping with the ironing*

while with no obvious improvement in its state He gave up. Then He had a go at a duvet cover which He thought might be more cooperative. He looked at us and said with uncharacteristic humility "I'm sure I haven't seen Heather having this difficulty". Eventually He found that switching the iron on made the whole enterprise more effective.

After a while the duvet cover was sort of done so He decided to put it onto the duvet. We followed Him into His bedroom because we didn't reckon that the show was over yet. Whichever way He tried to do it it seemed apparent that the duvet was quite a bit too big for the cover. That was strange He thought-it was the one that came off it. He laid the cover on the bed, then grabbing the leading edge of the duvet He crawled into

18

the cover with the duvet and tried to place the leading edge at the far end which seemed the logical place. He then crawled out. The duvet followed Him out, sliding neatly to the floor. He looked completely bewildered and tried again with the same result.

He gave up. He decided to sleep under an uncovered duvet and with crumpled sheets until such time as someone who knew about these things could unravel the mysteries or better still do it for Him.

We felt quite sorry for Him-briefly.

## July 15th

My resolve not to go fishing hasn't worked. He took us all to the Wylie again today. We went to the place where Fish learnt to swim chasing the water voles. Piglet was in one of his silly moods. When we got to the river there were cows in the field. What we didn't notice was the bull. Anyhow He pretends not to be worried by anything much so He sat on the bank with His back to the stock fence separating the animals from the river. Piglet took to dashing up and down the fence baiting the cows which wasn't a good idea. He took no notice and continued to put up His rod and was just finishing tying on a favourite fly when Piglet and MF started an unholy row very close to Him. He turned round and found Himself eye to eye with the bull with Piglet and MF snapping at its nose. The enraged animal was beginning to head butt the not too substantial fence posts which swayed and creaked. He leapt up and in the process managed to lodge a brand new "black ant" fishing fly into His thumb, the barb well inserted. Anyhow to cut a very long story short – the bull eventually lost interest and shuffled off back to his wives.

What we didn't know was that He had an appointment with Bob the vet back at the stables at a certain time during the afternoon. To get back to the car meant running the gauntlet of about 200 yards of unprotected field with a bull in an uncertain temper on the loose. He proved then how susceptible to fear He really was. It is almost unheard for Him to have His mobile phone with Him on these expeditions but for once He had. He rang the lovely Kate to deputise for Him with Bob explaining the circumstances of bull, unprotected field and a "black Ant" in his thumb. All she could do was howl with laughter which He thought a bit unsympathetic but she agreed to do it. After a very long time the bull lost interest in the pantomime beside the river so went back to work with his wives at the end of the field. With unusual haste He marched us out of the field with one or two anxious backwards glances.

Back at the farm the gardener, Anne, cut the shank of the 90p fly and He pulled it out of His thumb grumbling all the time about the expense– It's funny how really quite small sums of money trouble Him but He'll go flying a silly little helicopter at several hundred pounds a time without turning a hair.

**August 22nd**

He is still looking for a new horse. Poor Spider has been retired because of his tendons. I really like Spider because he is just a big equine hippy. He loves everyone and never gets fussed about anything. One evening He went into Spider's stable to change a rug and found a sparrow hawk perched on Spider's bottom. The hawk had been chasing doves while Spider munched away at his hay. The only time that Spider became seriously troubled was at clipping time every Autumn. Then he needed to be drugged which was a pantomime all on it's own. Kate and Karen did the clipping. They had about forty minutes before he started to come round. It was His job to hold the brute's head to stop him falling over! It became a spectator sport as various people from the village came to watch over the stable door. The last time this charade was performed, Karen's little girl, Lily was being potty trained so she was plonked on her potty in the box next to Spider while Kate and Karen got on with the clipping. After lunch we all went to somewhere in Somerset to look at a horse. As we entered the yard a nice looking horse put its head over its stable door. Kate said "if it's that one that is for sale, you are buying it – it's lovely". So He did. It's huge. Even bigger than Spider with a matching price tag. It might have been cheaper to buy the white one owned by Miss "North Sea" Ferry. We didn't get much of a say in the matter and just looked out of the car windows grumbling at the loose dogs in the yard. I get anxious that something the size of the new horse must eat a lot. Will my rations get cut down as a consequence?

**September 18th**

We went to get the new horse in the lorry today. We love going in the lorry because we can see all the other dogs outside along the way and get to have a go at them in a superior way. It was Pippa's Jack Russell "Beetle" who taught us to have a go from the comfort and safety of a vehicle. He doesn't like it because sometimes He doesn't anticipate the row and when we erupt His driving goes all to pot. The new horse is called Bess but has a posh name and is described as a show jumper in her passport. This all suggests that she is a good deal too smart for Him. His horses seem to get bigger and smarter in indirect proportion to His diminishing size and increasing scruffiness. It is said that since His wife Jane died He has become rather unkempt and tatty. My guess is that He spends so much money on horses and helicopters that there's none left for clothes but there again it might just be an innate scruffiness. He and His friend Bodget could start a competition for the least suave man in Dorset!

## November 28th

It was one of those glorious Winter days with steely blue skies and a mild frost. He went hunting for the first time this season. We were left with the prospect of a disciplined day under the direction of The Lovely Kate. To be fair she did take us in the car to the Meet which was at Trafalgar House not far from Salisbury. We were left in the car because I have an absolute thing about foxhounds. They are so big and pleased with themselves and lollop around the Meet being boisterous. Anyhow they make me mad so I have a go at them as they go past which irritates the Master.

At the end of the meet Kate gave Him his instructions which included no galloping, no jumping, and only two hours hunting. Well two and a half hours and eight jumps later He fell off at the gallop after a jump. The ground was pretty hard. It seemed that the stiff neck that had been troubling Him for some time was instantly cured and feeling not much more than silly He got back on. In the absence of a step ladder Angus Mann gave Him a leg up and off they all went again. However, two jumps and three quarters of an hour later the pain began to make itself felt so he made His way back to the lorry where someone's waiting groom put Bess in and pushed Him up into the cab to drive the 20 or more miles home.

Well what a cripple met us when He got home. Even Kate was nice to Him despite all her ignored instructions. At least the precious horse was in one piece. He left her to deal with Bess and staggered into the house. Give Him his due his first duty as He saw it was to give us a walk. Sadly He got halfway down the garden, tried to pass out, and had to return. He was in a bad way this time. He rang Nickie who came over and walked us while Julie helped Him off with his boots and generally nannied Him. Anyhow I think Kate really felt sorry for Him but later gave Him hell anyway. After a protracted feeding time due to His condition He tottered off to bed rather early.

## December 4th

It's worse than we thought – He really has made a mess of Himself this time. He's cracked His pelvis. After enduring increasing pain for a week even He began to panic and Kate took Him into Salisbury hospital. Being a Saturday, A & E was bulging with muscle bound rugby and football players with various injuries so Kate at least enjoyed herself. The doctor at the Hospital said he'd never seen such bruising and told Him to give up being such a fool at His age and find a more sedentary amusement. At about the same moment another friend of His came into A&E with a dislocated shoulder from a hunting accident with the Wilton. At this point the doctor erupted on the subject of hunting. Liz, His long suffering GP, merely sighed and told Him to revert to the painkillers left over from His broken ribs last season and keep up the whisky intake.

He's a pathetic sight hobbling around trying to walk us. So far as we are concerned it's a bit like a holiday because He can't catch up to admonish us so we can really quite literally run rings round Him. I have to say my arguments with Piglet are even more fun because they last longer and sometimes there's blood.

## December 12th

One of His best hunting mates came today to bring Him a couple of home made meals. He was more than usually grateful because the friend is suffering from cancer with a poor prognosis.

Not too surprisingly we get a pretty steady stream of friends to "see if He's alright" which usually degenerate into a top-off-bottle. Doesn't seem to matter what time of day. Some of the friends are kind enough to bring Him food. Usually it's Rachel from across the road and He calls her meals on legs. Yesterday someone saw Him walking us in Home Field (He hasn't been further than that yet) and enquired "who is that old codger walking JR's in the field?" It might have been kinder not to have repeated that comment to Him.

## December 14th

He went to a physiotherapist today. As He put it, He walked in and crawled out. He says He's not going there again. Anyhow He's improving slowly. We can see that our honeymoon period is nearly over. I had a huge argument with my cousin Mad Dillon. He is by any standards completely batty. We can cope with that but Dillon overdid it today. After his usual fifty-yard dash up the lawn barking at nothing in particular he found one of my toys and brought it back. At first I thought it quite decent of Him until I realised he was in fact keeping it and killing it so I went for Him. Karen, who has a part share in Dillon tried to separate us; He tried to chuck water at us and missed, more or less drenching Karen instead. I kept a firm grip on Dillon's throat while Dillon had a firm grip on my right ear – impasse – after a bit we both rather forgot what the argument was about and gave up. I strutted into the house while Dillon strutted about on the lawn in a rather aimless way. Actually as fights go it was quite a good one. Better than the ones I have with Piglet because he is such a drip and gives up so easily. Anyhow Kate always intervenes which is pathetic really.

My Mother is definitely getting middle aged and boring. She hadn't bitten Him for ages until today. She was quietly chewing her way through a cricket ball that she had found under the sideboard in the dining room. He tried to retrieve it. There was no sense in that really. It was bound to end in tears because it was a golden opportunity for her to have a go at Him. Anyhow as He hates cricket why was He so worried about the imminent demise of the ball. He took it quite badly and tried to retaliate but she ducked out of the way and legged it to her sanctuary under the chest on the landing. She can still just squeeze under it.

## December 20th

He has decided to go to the farm in Northumberland for Christmas. It looks as if just about everything hurts judging by the way He moves but He says that the Mercedes is so well designed that driving is one of His least painful activities. Well it is a seven-hour drive under normal conditions but the old relic is not in normal condition so He decided to break the journey at an hotel in Derbyshire.

I don't suppose they were quite ready for the rag, tag and bobtail crew that tottered up to check-in. MF, because she has a conviction that everyone wants to meet her, rushed off to greet her adoring public just as soon as He opened the car door. We could trace her progress by the squeals of delight from the children who she encountered and the recriminatory yells from staff and adult customers. He of course couldn't follow her as fast as He would have liked and tottered, somewhat supported by a stick, in the vague direction of the protests. By the time He caught up with her she was doing a circuit of the dining room and as He approached she went to ground under a heavily draped table. The dining couple looked on bemused and a little bit alarmed as He, not able to bend too far for fear of breaking in two presumably, tried to scoop her out with his stick. All she did was to bite the end of it. In the meantime I was able to get a bit familiar with the rest of the establishment, which revealed itself to be an overheated Victorian mansion of dubious architectural merit.

Eventually MF emerged from under the table encouraged by some deft footwork by the two diners and a carefully aimed whack from His stick. You could tell that she had had a good time by the contented look on her face and her tail which remained defiantly erect like a flag of victory. She had certainly made her mark and no actress had ever made such an entrance or exit.

After our supper which we had in the back of the car He attached us to leads and took us to His bedroom which was superheated. He tried to open a window without success. After surviving life in His cold, drafty house in Dorset an hermetically sealed, overheated hotel bedroom was not to our liking. He had brought our travelling beds in earlier and indicated them to us. Fish jumped onto the four-poster bed while I curled up on a nice comfortable looking chair. He was obviously too tired to argue because He merely looked at us wearily and tottered out to dinner.

**December 21st**

When we got to the farm Sid was amazed by His condition. He looked so incredibly decrepit compared to His normal sprightly self. We have found that with Him in this condition we can run pretty wild without let or hindrance so we scooped up Sid's dog Nearly Dead and went off to explore. Not much has changed since our last visit, in the house at any rate. It's just as scruffy as ever and locked into the mid 20th century which means that no one really knows where anything or anyone is most of the time. That suits us. There is a rather straight road running past the farm along which cars travel at an alarming speed. It seems that some of our predecessors have had some close encounters on it so He gets pretty agitated when we go out. Actually between the house and the road are some wonderful barns which traditionally house hay and straw and sometimes farm stock. Well obviously there are almost unlimited opportunities to find rats or at worst to find evidence of them. One or two rabbits have been sighted in there too. All this gives Him palpitations because of the proximity of the road and His blood pressure notches up a good few points. It's quite gratifying the way He worries about us.

He started the task of unshipping all our stuff out of the car and His own modest suitcase. It seems that He has perfected the art of travelling light after all His years of bachelorhood. Pretty soon He was worn out and getting tottery so He had to sit down for the first whisky in front of a nice fire. Sid is pretty good to Him considering.

## December 25th

As if this place hasn't got enough horses one way and another. He's gone and given the children a scruffy little pony for Christmas. Shrimpy looked a bit bemused and Katie made cooing noises at it when He paraded it on the lawn. It goes by the rather grand name of Carlton. They all had to have a ride round the lawn before getting back to the essentials of food and sweets.

I expect He has unrealistic ideas of taking them hunting on this poor little animal. I suppose it would be quite handy for Him to have a family member to scrape Him off the ground after the inevitable spills.

## December 26th

He insisted on going to the Boxing Day Meet which is held just down the road at a pub in which He has disgraced Himself a good few times in the past. His good friend Dave, who used to be the publican, made so much money out of Him that he has retired to Goa. His place has been taken by Dave's Brother who had not heard about Him. Quite soon he too will be able to retire somewhere exotic from the dubious return of the native.

At the Meet we were kept on leads. Fish would have tried to make friends with the hounds who would have regarded her as not much more than a rat sized morsel and I would have tried to kill them. He did a tour of the field hailing His old mates who are also getting pretty decrepit. They had to show Him that despite Dave's defection to India the pub hadn't changed much. There seemed to be a marked reduction of His old friends mounted but plenty on foot holding glasses. It is traditional that on Boxing Day they draw the coverts on this farm. He wanted to watch so back we went.

At the farm we watched as the field took the jumps He had built decades ago and which now tended to disintegrate if hit even mildly. He found it all very amusing and He laughed His awful laugh when people fell off which smacks of humbug.

## December 30th

Once again He decided that to do the whole journey back to Dorset in one go might be a bit too much for Him so we stopped at a rather nice place just outside Nottingham. When He was at Cirencester College He had a good friend who lived near Nottingham. He was quite anxious to find Him. So in His usual way He sailed up to the nice lady who owned this hotel and expected her to know exactly who He was talking about and where he now lived. She just looked bemused as she gave Him His key and frowned at us. It had been snowing quite hard so He was even more at risk of falling over thus damaging yet more bits of His rapidly disintegrating frame. He felt entirely vindicated for choosing this hotel when a customer arrived in a helicopter amid a blizzard of blown snow.

This time we were given a room on the ground floor in a wing at the back; presumably to keep us out of harm's way. It didn't work.

There was a fishpond. MF can't help jumping into ponds rather in the same way He can't refuse an offer of a whisky. The owner was not amused and not only reprimanded Him for allowing her to do it (as if He could have stopped her) but made Him dry her before re-entering the hotel. There is always an assortment of old clothes knocking about in the bowels of the car so He gave Fish a token rub down with an old sweater.

We were shut in His room while He had his supper which probably wasn't a good idea. MF instantly jumped onto the bed. The one bit He had neglected to clean after her plunge was her feet and legs. She left perfect footprints all over the nice white bed linen.

In the meantime He was being gratifyingly chatted up in the bar by the owner. This massaged his ego no end until He discovered she mistook Him for someone famous. He took to bullshitting with the helicopter man. When He got back to the room He nearly self-destructed at the state of the place. I had discovered a giant bar of Toblerone that Heather had given Him for Christmas. I had done it fair justice. The carpet positively sparkled with tiny bits of silver paper. Fish lay on her back on the newly re-designed bed cover with her feet in the air waiting for Him to admire her disgusting tummy as usual. We thought He was going to have a stroke. There was a lot of yelling and bad language so we got under the bed which seemed to irritate Him even more.

He paid the bill that night and we left very early the next day. Another nice hotel we won't be able to revisit unless we all go in disguise.

## March 21st

A gloom has descended on everyone. He has decided to move back to the farm in Northumberland. We suppose He has run out of romantic possibilities in this neck of the woods. There have been a lot of people coming to the house today because He has decided to have a party to say goodbye to His friends. He is getting another big tent for the occasion. And what a tent it is going to be. Fresh from Morocco. This one won't fall down in a hurry. There were all sorts of discussion about Moorish lanterns and flooring.

They have fixed a date for this bash in June which seems very far off. We got forgotten so Kate took us for a walk to Little Wood where she lost Piglet who has taken to running off into the jungle and forgetting where he is. It's rather sad really because he has been running round these woods all his life and he still gets lost. When this happens he sits on his wide blunt end and lets out tragic wails. He gets so carried away with his plight and the musicality of his cries that he fails to hear Kate calling so he gets more and more anxious. After a time while he was gasping for breath he heard Kate and returned with his wagger going nineteen to the dozen. We all think that he is one of those rare thick as a plank JRs.

*Me and Uncle Piglet*

**April 9th**

He bundled MF and me into the car and took us to the New Forest again. I rather enjoy it all but MF finds the long trek across the heather moors between woods very boring. Her little legs can't cope with the deep going so to speak whereas I bound along. There is a special place that He goes to often where He can pick sweet chestnuts and me and MF can exhaust ourselves chasing rabbits. On the way there we pass a big house where a friend of His mother used to live so that gives an idea how long ago that must have been. Anyway today much to our astonishment and His delight a helicopter took off from the garden just as we were passing and roared away to the North. He was transfixed. It took us a good few minutes to bring Him down to earth. You could almost see the fantasies whirling about in His head. There is absolutely no guarantee that He will not suddenly convert a shed on the estate into a hangar and install His own wretched machine. That will be that because He is bound to crash and you don't pop along to A and E for a patch up job after crashing a helicopter.

**April 10th**

He is impulsive. That little brush with a helicopter yesterday made Him rush off to Bournemouth airport as soon as He could after our walk. At least He has the decency to think of us first or is it habit. I try not to speculate.

It was not a good idea. He should be made to have a cooling off period after the episode in the New Forest. It seems that He is coming up for His test for a pilot's licence so He had to do a dummy run so to speak. He started to day dream during the flight and went wildly off course. Then when asked by the senior instructor how He would work out His position He replied that He would go down and read the road signs. Not a popular thing to have said. Well it went even more wrong. On the way back to the heliport He very nearly crashed right in front of the control tower. His instructor was heard to mumble "You are the reason I've got to find another job". Hardly a vote of confidence.

He returned to the house rather quieter than usual and we had a quiet walk and a quiet supper and He had a quiet evening snoozing in front of the television.


**April 17th**

He's back to His old self. A friend has given Him some peculiar looking bantam hens. They were in a coop at the end of the garden but today He decided that it was time that they found out what the real world was like so He liberated them. Well what sport. Me and the others chased them all over the place. They are tiny but one managed to fly into the Laburnam tree and got itself caught up in the rose He calls Creeping Cleric but which is catalogued as Rambling Rector. Needless to say He got a bit apoplectic. He really doesn't need to get so excited.

We know perfectly well that they are not really live targets but sometimes one forgets. He calmed down after a bit and tried to entice the hapless bird out of the tree. It didn't work so He rang Tess and arranged to take us there for a walk instead. Tess has a big bumbling golden Retriever called Josh. We love him. He is so chaotic. Another of those dogs that look as if their coats were a bad buy at a charity shop.

Tess has bought a piano which quite coincidentally was made by His great Grandfather in London. She comes from a very musical family. Apparently all He knows about the instrument is that it has alternate black and white keys. About a million years ago His friend Mikey Portman taught Him to play chop sticks which He forgot quite quickly. Mikey then died. We have to assume the events were not connected.

## May 21st

He has had a series of removal firms round today giving all the junk the once over for an estimate for transporting it to Northumberland. The representatives all looked a bit baffled as He led them from untidy room to even more untidy room then into the garden to view the disintegrating benches and statuary. There are an inordinate number of pots ranging from quite modest to frankly grotesque. All of them contain much loved plants including His precious pelargonium which Bodget tried to steal and which He retrieved from a rather grand urn on the terrace at Bodget's house. It seems that on one of Bodget's visits to Him round about the magic hour he went home across the garden through Home field. On his way he helped himself to the plant. Needless to say He didn't notice until the effects of the tincture had worn off some time later.

The books in the house alone would occupy a fair sized van. Perhaps the last straw was when He showed them the stables and tack room. One removals man thought he would have to transport the horses and looked as if he might break out in an attack of hives at any moment. There also seems to be a slight mistrust of us JRs by the estimators. Perhaps one or two of our relatives have resented the notion of a house move. They looked at us through the corner of their eyes. We followed them about sniffing at their trousers. One of them gave a slight backward kick which MF neatly fended off. I would have had his ankle. He was lucky there.

## June 5th

He has had the estimates for the removals. A great gloom has descended. Occasionally at times of stress like this He gets into the car with us and takes us for a good walk somewhere fun. And so it was today. We went to His old haunt in the New Forest again. We walked from Verely to Backley and back again. I love that walk through the heather and the woods. MF is less enthusiastic because she prefers woodland the whole time. He has bought some walking boots which are far too small. They gave Him such jip that I thought He might give up. That would have been silly. MF and I couldn't have got Him back to the car.

When we got back home a lorry had delivered huge rolls of bubble wrap and tissue paper by the ton. It was all put in the garden room. He is beginning to look distracted. He's wandering around the house making lists on bits of paper and then falls over one of us cursing. Any one would think we wanted to move and were forcing it on Him. If the truth is known we quite like this haphazard life watching His equally chaotic life unfold. He puts the lists on the kitchen table which then get lost amongst the cooking utensils as He prepares His supper.

Piglet has disgraced himself today. In one of his fizzy fits he found himself on the bench which goes with the kitchen table and thence onto the table itself. The excitement got to his bladder and he managed to have a prolonged pee up there! The table is dish shaped because the Frenchman who made it was not much of a carpenter according to Him so there was quite a lake in the centre.

Just for once He didn't go mad but I bet it would have been another story if Piglet's owner hadn't been a more than usually pretty blonde. The table has had a terrific scrub with all sorts of disinfectants and even if He isn't the most fastidious of people He must have taken a few surface layers off by now. Not before time I suspect so in a way Piglet did him a service but it is doubtful whether He will see it that way.

## June 8th

Nick has come for a long weekend with a new girlfriend, Emma. She is a tall, good-looking, Scottish girl with long legs and a stride to match. To be honest she looks a bit daunting. She frogmarched us for a walk and it was not easy keeping up with her. Nick is a big bloke but even he found her a bit strident. It seems that her family own chunks of the Scottish Highlands where they strangle twelve pointers with their bare hands before breakfast having stalked them for a few hours just for the exercise. During the course of conversation about this and that, He mentioned Piglet's indiscretion vis-à-vis the kitchen table which is documented in MF's book and everyone laughed.

## June 9th

Nick's mad dog Hector is always with Him so today we all went on a walk leaving Him at home to prepare the evening meal. We went ratting along the big hedge along side the lower park. Hector is a very strange member of the terrier clan. As MF pointed out in her book his teeth seem to have been randomly inserted at all sorts of angles amd his hind legs are without doubt from the wrong parts box. He is hopeless at chasing anything and even if he caught anything he would have to sieve it through the wonky tooth arrangement.

By the time we got back to the house He was chopping up vegetables on the table without the aid of a chopping board. Emma looked on in horror and disbelief. Eventually she plucked up the courage to offer Him a chopping board. "No thanks" He replied, "the table is a brilliant giant chopping board" indicating the full seven feet of French timber with a flamboyant sweep of His hand. He carried on chopping. Once again she offered and once again He refused. She didn't enjoy the meal and she never returned. He still chops everything on the table. No one has died or even gone a funny colour as a result of eating in the house-yet.
We all believe that He wasn't that keen on Emma anyhow. He referred to her as "Same Arm, Same Leg". It is possible that the whole episode was a charade to discourage her from returning.

## June 10th

The house has taken on the appearance of an obstacle course. He has moved the rolls of bubble wrap into various rooms and has begun the task of wrapping all His pictures. We find it rather fun and with my long legs I can jump onto a roll and then regard it as a stepping-stone to the next one so to speak. Fish and Pig whizz around the place trying to catch me. Now and then I fall off the rather slippery surface and then we have chasing games round the stacks of books that now also litter the place. There is an upside to this moving process I suppose.

Kate and Geors came in to help wrap the pictures. They fooled about popping the bubbles and generally being giggly and silly. He got a bit grumpy because His pictures are His pride and joy and if the truth is known quite valuable. The girls just laughed. As each picture came off the wall, so another family of spiders was exposed and scuttled for cover behind something else. I quite like spiders because they are good quarry. One has to admire the way they can still make it to the skirting board when one has relieved them of quite a few of their legs.

## June 11th

We all went to see Tess again which is only a couple of miles across the fields. Tess has a son who is good fun and we played with him while the two of them had coffee. Then we all went for a walk through the woods near Tess's house. Josh, Tess's retriever, came too. There is a very active shoot there so we were able to get a few pheasants off the ground in no uncertain fashion. It was just as well that we didn't run into the evil tempered game keeper with whom He has had the odd run in in the past.

On our way home it began to rain, which doesn't normally bother anyone but Piglet decided to frisk a 40 acre field of well grown oilseed rape. The bad tempered game keeper has a partridge release pen on the boundary which erupts with birds when you go near it. Well given Piglet's ability to get lost in Little Wood which he knows like the back of his hand it wasn't too surprising when he got hopelessly lost in the rape. After about fifteen minutes of Him yelling and whistling He decided that Piglet would find his own way home so we trudged off back to the house.

When an hour had gone by and still no sign of Piglet He began to panic. I suspect the thought of Kate's wrath spurred Him on. He locked us up in the Swamp which is His name for our bedroom and returned to the field on His bicycle. I'm not sure why the bike was pressed into action. By now the rain was fairly drenching. He began to whistle through his fingers which is pretty penetrating.

Eventually Piglet, who had been going round in circles for nearly two hours, appeared. He cycled back over the fields with a relieved Piglet at His side.

All Kate said when He told her of the excitement was that they would have found Piglet at harvest time! You see I was right: you really can't trust the fairer sex.

**June 20th**

The village gave Him a surprise leaving party in the hotel. He, as might
be imagined, completely overdid the whisky and then mixed it with
wine. There were flattering speeches which if the truth be known left
Him quite emotional. He made an attempt at a reply which consisted of
indecipherable gargling noises and after the meal they all retired to the
smoking room where He subsided onto a sofa with a port and the young
postmistress with whom He behaved rather badly. She goes pink when she
sees Him now.

His own party isn't far away. He has decided to ask the entire village and
a good few other people from round about too. I expect it is an attempt to
placate all those who have been tormented by Him over the years.

He spent hours today writing out invitations. We really get pretty short
shrift at the moment because He is so preoccupied with it all. Geors is
away on one of her trips, this time to India and Harry is being a film
director somewhere so He is on His own most of the time. It will be quite
a gathering. Kate reckons that she is, by adoption, a member of His family
and is helping a good deal. She likes a party and gets to invite her family
and friends too.

**June 22nd**

We were bundled into the car today and taken to Salisbury where we then
got left in the multi-storey car park. Piglet has learned to set up howling
as soon as He leaves us and we join in just for a laugh. In the early days
of this ploy He would come racing back to shut us up. He always looked
about Him anxiously in case people thought He was abusing us. Now He
ignores us but it does draw a pleasing audience. Pippa, another girl friend
taught her JR "Beatle" to bark at other dogs on the pavement from the
safety of the car and we have cottoned on to what an amazing game that
is too. Normally He sees the other dogs on the roadside before we do and
He says something to distract us which sometimes works. Today He was
dreaming and Piglet, who was on the perch let out a piercing yell just as
we were coming up to the roundabout south of Salisbury and He nearly
ran into a bus. Piglet got cuffed quite hard.

He returned with armfuls of things for the party. It seems that He has
cleaned out Threshers on a sale or return agreement for lorry loads of

drink. I am glad that it is all being delivered because the ageing Mercedes would never have hauled it the twenty or so miles home. He has bought two hoggets from a farming friend who lives at the back of beyond at the top of Cranborne Chase. These He intends to spit roast on the estate spit made by Bodget's side-kick Alistair. Alistair is the architect of not doing very much for decades and getting away with it. Indeed he has become an icon of positive inactivity. In years to come he will become a standard university study subject. He is, along with Bodget, a bit of a role model as he puffs away on his pipe while watching other people work. Alistair says that the sheep should be precooked in an army field kitchen first and then merely finished off on the spit.

## June 24th

The army are busy! So we all went to see His chum who owns a bakery in a nearby village and He has arranged to put the sheep into the baking oven for a few hours on the day of the party. After that we went with Him to see His doctor to get an update on His injuries. If I am honest He does not complain about them but He has been having some pain recently and has put it off for as long as possible because He is such a coward. Anyhow we sat in the car and serenaded anyone within earshot with our usual dog-a-wauling as He calls it. That brought out some of the customers and staff from the surgery. He emerged looking a bit worried. It seems He didn't

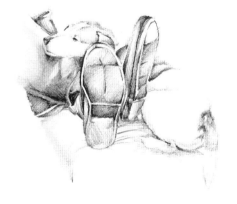

see His usual doctor who, knowing Him as well as she does, listens sympathetically and then prescribes painkillers washed down with whisky which seems to work a treat. This time He saw one of the other doctors who scared Him half to death with dire warnings about blood pressure and strokes and so on. He tottered out and we went home where He wrote the doctor a rude letter telling him that He would rather die than consult him again.

## June 25th

A slight panic has set in because the band for the party say they are performing in Belgium the night before His party and might not make it back. He has bribed them enough and it seems that even if they get no sleep they will turn up. All this stress will put Him into the doctor's surgery again. Now is not the moment for the stroke.

## June 27th

Great excitement. A tatty old Land Rover arrived this morning and disgorged a rugger player and the rest of the front row who set-to unloading a Moroccan tent. We love seeing this lot because not only do they bring their own brand of recalcitrant Springer Spaniel but He is so preoccupied that we get away with just about anything.

We and the Springer went runabout and June had to ring Him up to tell Him that we were up Laundry Lane and aiming South. You could hear Him yelling for us a mile off so we legged it. It's a wonderfully scruffy bit of the estate and there are sheds full of Gaeton's rubbish where we can rootle about disturbing mice, rats and especially Gaeton's cat. We were careful not to chase the cat too much. Gaeton's wife owns the estate so we would have been chucked out before our official departure date if anything terminal was to happen to the moggy.

By the evening the tent was more or less up. It is certainly very pretty. I had to attend to each pole so to speak and He chased me off fearing an electrical excitement since the wiring for the lights went up them and He was worried that the whole thing would go up in a mushroom cloud of smoke. He's an awful worrier.

## June 28th

Harry drifted in, in his usual artistic daze. The garden certainly looks very pretty at this time of year so Harry started off on the right foot by commenting nicely on it but rather blew it by asking casually if there was anything he could do. As He had just spent heaven knows how many weeks preparing for this event more or less on His own with occasional help from the Lovely Kate He didn't take Harry's offer too well. Harry, who is a sensitive flower, got an earful so went to stay with his Grandmother in Hampshire.

He continued to put what He always referred to as His "fairy lights" in the trees and all over the garden trellis-work. Over the years additions had been made to the string which started quite modestly as a few lights to decorate the veranda. Now it stretches for fifty or more yards and has been cobbled up by Him. The whole thing frightens us all because He knows absolutely nothing about electrics. He did a test run which surprisingly didn't blow the whole village.

## June 29th

Well the great day has dawned. He left really early taking me and M.F. We went miles into the hills on Cranborne Chase to get the hoggets. His farmer friend was leaving for Salisbury to catch a train to London. He had forgotten about the sheep. With 100 plus people coming to supper He nearly had a seizure. Fortunately they found a couple of dead sheep which were hanging in a shed ready for someone else. They were bundled into the boot of the car which had been spread with newspaper. Meantime, M F and I escaped and found the shed where they kept other corpses. What with His appointment at the bakery and His friend's date with a London train it all got pretty fraught. This stroke must be imminent.

We took the corpses to the bakery where they were fed into the oven. Then we went back home where He had to furnish the tent, getting chairs from the village hall and stripping the house and garden of all useful dining furniture. Geors and Kate were there fooling about and helping in their fashion. Later on, after a lie down at his grandmother's house, Harry made a comeback just as He returned from the bakery with the now sizzling sheep. They had to be got from the car to the spit which had been set up by Alistair under the laburnham tree. In a conciliatory gesture Harry offered to help carry the beasts, now oozing juices. His offer was readily accepted so Harry went off to get protective clothing and reappeared wearing a Barbour back to front and a pair of yellow Marigold gloves. Harry's fastidiousness is legendary so everyone had a good laugh.
The somnolent band appeared in need of restorative cups of tea. They set up their instruments under the veranda. By this time Heather had arrived so she and Kate helped to arrange the food on the dining room table and at last He was able to breathe a sigh of relief followed by an enormous whisky.

It was a heavenly June night. He allowed us to mingle with the guests and once supper was on the way we did very well. People danced on the lawn or sat around in groups gossiping. Pippa's two sons were allowed to have a go on the band's instruments. What with His "fairy lights" the band and all the lights on in the house the inevitable loud bang threw every one into darkness. He didn't seem the least bit concerned and fortunately the village electrician who was a guest came to the rescue. Much talk of six inch nails. After a lot of embarrassing dancing by Him who, by this time, was well lubricated. He insisted on some Elvis Presley to moans from at least half of the village while the geriatrics, even those not known for vulgar displays of dancing, got to their feet while the young had a good laugh.

We got pretty tired and retired to the Swamp eventually. Heaven knows when He got to bed.

## June 30th

Heather came today to try to put some order into the place. The house is a shambles. There are what look like dead bodies everywhere. There was even one person asleep in a bath. He took us for what can only be described as a dazed totter out into Home Field. On the way up the garden He looked wearily at the empties lying in the flower beds, burnt out candles on the wine spattered tables in the tent and just winced. Poor Heather who had been at the party herself gave the whole place a tired look and set to clearing glasses, plates and cutlery into the hard working dishwasher. We came back to the sound of her navigating the Dyson round the furniture. She just kept going. He doesn't know how lucky He is.

It is hard to believe but He decided that as a farewell gesture He would hire a four seater helicopter and give anyone who wanted it a joy ride. We were all pleased to see that He had had the sense to arrange for a professional pilot to drive the thing. Without doubt He would not have been in the right condition. It arrived in Home Field at the appointed hour and began ferrying people round the estate. The hotel guests came out to watch and every now and then He had a rather wobbly go Himself.

## July 3rd

The removals people arrived at 8am. It was a dull, drizzly sort of day. I've never seen such an enormous lorry. The foreman walked round the house and eventually shook his head saying "It'll never all fit in the lorry guv". At this remark the stroke took a lurch closer. He went a funny colour. The man must have seen the look of panic on His face. "We'll try but it's going to be a tight fit". All the doors and gates were of necessity left open so me and the gang had a rare old time charging in and out of the house and garden. We even did a few circuits inside the removals lorry which took up most of the stable yard. It's quite gratifying that He does worry about us, the move and so on but I expect the expense will be highest on His worry list. At the critical moment Tess turned up looking fresh and delectable to wish Him bon voyage, I suppose. Then the immobiliser on her car jammed so that she was obstructing the lorry. They pushed her car out of the way. He lent her the Subaru and rather ungraciously sent her home.

Eventually Kate arrived, presumably to view the perspiring removals men who apparently didn't come up to snuff so she took us for a walk. I reckon she has a goodish time because one assumes that she gets paid for this rather pleasant lifestyle. It slightly shook Him one day when her mother who works in a pet shop in Blandford told Him that Kate was lucky to have such a good "Sugar Daddy"! I don't think He had seen Himself in that role.

The foreman of the gang told Him that they would indeed never get it all in by a long way. He rang Pickfords and told them in no uncertain terms that they had better get everything to Northumberland or He would set His lawyer friend Gavin onto them. By the time we got back with Kate there was another enormous lorry filling up.

## July 4th

We spent the night at Bodget's house. We slept in the car amongst all His very precious and most personal junk. He didn't sleep much for worrying about not sleeping before a long journey. That's typical of Him. He can get so relaxed driving the silly little helicopter that he wanders miles off course but worries himself silly about a long car journey. As an illustration of that, on His first cross country solo in the Robinson which was planned in detail He found Himself flying over Salisbury instead of Exeter. He only noticed when He saw the Cathedral spire looming up which gave Him some sort of clue that He was a bit off course. We get to wondering if we will ever get to there because He has to stop for a little sleep every now and then. His doctor friend Tim suggested that He might have a touch of narcolepsy. That scared Him. After a hurried breakfast we set off leaving all sorts of things in Bodget's kitchen some of which were rather important - like our supper and dog bowls and biscuits and, as far as He was concerned, most importantly a bottle of whisky. We went to Worcestershire to Sid's house there. It was all becoming quite an adventure. The horses had been sent up to the farm some days ago in a huge Eric Gillie lorry which looked so luxurious I rather wish I had gone with them. It was a good deal cleaner and smarter than His car.

# The New Life

### July 5th

Journey's end. We have moved back to the family farm in the North. His "ex", who is known as Sid, has been living there in His absence running amok in Dorset. His romantic life leaves most of us breathless. Sid was there to greet us with her two dogs.

There is "Nearly Dead", a curious little patchwork quilt of a dog but very welcoming and friendly and "Brain Dead", a whippet of beautiful form but with few connected neurones. His comment was that "you can't connect what isn't there" which is a bit harsh we think but not too far off the mark. The first thing He did was to take us for a walk. We were so excited to be away from the chaos of the last few days and out of the car that me and MF ran wild. The Bomb field has a tall standing crop of oilseed rape and a good few new smells so we both got thoroughly lost in it. He got terribly agitated with the memory of Piglet in the 40 acres in Dorset. This field is about the same size so panic really did set in and we could hear it in His voice so we capitulated and came back. He was visibly shaken. I think His nerves are a bit shot.

In some ways the farm is better than Dorset. The house is just as tatty so nothing can be spoiled there but there are endless farm buildings which

*"Nearly Dead"*

promise endless investigation. We sleep by the Aga here which is a good deal better than the Swamp in Dorset. There is an incredibly old cat called Biba who lives in the scullery. She belonged to His mother so that gives an indication of her vintage because His Mother has been dead a goodish time. Biba is a bit nervous of us. If she only knew how the cat Blot in Dorset ruled us.

The horses have nice stables in one of the sheds but are out to grass now of course. So we are pretty well all self-contained.

## July 20th

He and Nick flew to Southampton this evening to fetch the lorry which is sitting on the estate full of some of the tattiest junk. We all think this is a bit risky as neither of them has driven a lorry very far before and there is some doubt as to whether Nick has ever driven one at all. When he was in the army in Germany Nick was famous for navigating his little tank the wrong way up an autobahn. This does not bode well for the proposed journey.

Well the plane was five hours late. They were to stay with Bodget who was going to fetch them from the airport. He had asked Mrs Bodget to invite one or two of His friends including Tess round for supper. He and Nick arrived at Southampton at about the time normal people go home after a supper party and sure enough they had. It is really decent of Mr and Mrs Bodget to amuse and feed His friends for an evening. Having got to know Him they probably aren't the least bit surprised at anything connected with Him.

## July 21st

He picked up the things that they managed to leave behind last time at Bodget's house including our food and some feed bowls and then left some more behind. Bodget had drunk the whisky. His friend Lynn had given Him a couple of Runner ducks as a leaving present so their first port of call was to her house to fetch Gregory and Peck as He had called them. The poor creatures were put into a biggish cardboard box with a bowl of water. They were then inserted through the Jockey door into the bowels of the lorry where He had made a space for them and that was that. The first few miles were distinctly rough with Nick thinking he was driving his yuppie Saab. From time to time He got out to check that Greg and Peck were still alive. Needless to say their water was anywhere but in its bowl.

After about nine hours of pretty continuous driving they arrived back at the farm. He said that driving an ageing lorry the entire length of England was exhausting conveniently forgetting that Nick had done practically all of it.

This is the first time that we have met Gregory & Peck. They are on the kitchen lawn in a rather makeshift wire cage with five young chickens. MF and I chased all the wretched things round the pen in a flurry of feathers and downy fluff. It's really good sport until He came out and started bellowing. Sid looked on anxiously. I wonder if her hair has gone that colour anticipating this upheaval in her previously quiet and ordered life.

## August 1st

He has put an old tatty chicken house into a corner of the farmyard. This is on the exact route of the Roman road which crosses the farm. What with Roman paving and His wrecked shoulders from falling off horses the posts that support the chicken wire for the pen haven't penetrated very far so the whole contraption is pretty rickety. He has installed what He rather grandly described as a Dorset gate which is an excuse for not doing a proper gate at all, just a bit of movable wire on a post. Sid is good the way she says nice things about His DIY work. In no time at all someone will have to come and do it all again but properly. Greg and Peck have been installed along with a sort of galvanised bath tub for a pond. We can ogle them from outside. They can escape our attentions by nipping round the back of the old hen house. It drives Him mad because they do that when He comes out to put them to bed. The adult chickens, on the other hand, live in a magnificent house opposite. They get to roam wherever they want to all day. We have learnt not to actually kill chickens.

## September 10th

He really has got us baffled this time. He's been off to Morpeth and hired a turf stripper and is now busy taking the turf off the lower sloping lawn. He's piling the rolled up turf all over the place and the garden has bizarre pyjama stripes of strips of grass where He didn't get it quite right. He told one of the tenants when she enquired that He was installing a swimming pool. She shuffled off looking troubled and later admitted that she believed Him but just questioned the wisdom of an open air pool in Northumberland. I don't even think Sid knows what's going on – she went to the little office upstairs and gazed out of the window as if to say, "now what's He up to?" It may well be that she is wondering what she has taken on again. It is said that she is now on blood pressure pills.

## September 12th

We went for a long walk today, which included a good long look at the river which runs through the next door farm. It was sunny and hot and there were a few flies on the water. A good sized trout rose. He nearly self destructed and you could just see His mind working on whether to surreptitiously poach or go and talk to the owner. I think that the thought of being in the local paper as a poacher rather appealed to Him but He hasn't been back long enough to shoulder the storm it might provoke. MF has a passion for water. She plunges in which isn't very popular on the Wylie but He is so indulgent that He rarely says anything. In contrast I hate the stuff. I can't even stand going through puddles which is a bit limiting on this damp old farm. Anyhow she plunged in and swam to the other side which is a Woodland Trust property with lovely trees and a very high bank with a sheer drop of about forty feet into the river. Well He got apoplectic when He saw her plunging through the undergrowth on the side of the bank visualising her sudden descent into the river. In the event she returned looking pleased with herself. I, on the other hand, went frisking through the gorse bushes on our side and came up trumps with quite a few of Cookie's pheasants and a roe deer.

The return walk to the farm is only a mile or so but it is mainly through long grass which tests short legs a good bit. MF is blessed with absurdly short legs and it really is a struggle sometimes for her. She has had the odd strange unexplained fainting fit recently which is terribly distressing for Him but doesn't seem to phase her at all. Well she had one on the way home today. It is quite touching really. He sits on the grass cradling her goofy looking head in His arms while saying soppy things to her. I find these episodes a bit unnerving but I have this little nagging thought that maybe she does it on purpose just to make sure that He is still as besotted as ever.

*Me avoiding the stream*

## September 16th

We were playing in the garden today rushing round with Brain Dead and poor MF had another turn. He was visibly shaken because we all know that she is really the love of His life. He scooped her up and took her to the vet in Morpeth. It seems that she will have to stay in all day for Francis, the vet, to give her the works. He, of course, is pacing about the place as if she was about to give birth again. I don't think that it is fair that the local vet is a pretty blonde. He will spend a quite unnecessary amount of time finding excuses to take us there.

MF is back from the vet. They can't find anything the matter. Who knows it might just be a reaction to Him or the move or the cold air in this part of the world.

## October 1st

Now we know what all that turf stripping was for. He met a man at a country show in the summer. The man turned up today in an enormous digger and is busy terracing the lawn. It's a matter of 'cut and fill', which is one of His favourite expressions. It reminds Him that He was once a Chartered Surveyor. He was "defrocked" as He puts it, for failing to pay the subscription. In truth He's quite proud of being sacked because He can now stick to land agency. Sometimes when writing to clients who know how barmy He is He adds the words "Defrocked" on the letter heading. He thinks that is a terrific joke. One of His wives said that people only employed Him because He is "cheap, cheerful and safely potty."

The tenant is now certain that an out-door swimming pool is imminent. She comes from darkest Tyneside so is not all that surprised by anything that happens in what to her is this rural lunatic asylum that she finds herself in.

Now all the soil that was at the bottom of the lawn is at the top. In truth He's making a croquet lawn at the bottom and a rose garden at the top. I have to say I'm not all that surprised that Sid's on blood pressure pills. Each day brings its own crop of surprises. She says that His insane desire to have a new project almost on a daily basis will eventually kill her.

We are kept out of the garden for the time being in case we get dug up along with the soil. The whole place is a shambles. One can just hope that it doesn't rain otherwise it would take on the aspect of a first World War battle field.

## November 8th

My relative youthfulness means that from time to time I am inclined to be a bit bouncy with Nearly Dead and she doesn't care for it. It is not that she does much. She looks bored and now and then shows her gums-most of her teeth have long since dropped out. Today we went to the wood near the house where we often go. It is not too far from the farm. He never fails to tell us, and anyone else within ear shot, that He planted it back in the dark ages as He puts it. It is quite fun because it contains very sporting rabbits which wait for us to turn up and then leg it down their burrows. They really can shift and not even the fleet of foot Brain Dead can catch them. Today Brain Dead proved how apt her name is. She ran smack into a tree chasing a rabbit. She lay on the ground looking more than usually dazed. Sid came over all maternal and made soppy noises. Nearly Dead stood by thinking what buffoons all us young things are. Quite soon Brain Dead came round, got up and raced off again as if nothing had happened. In the Bomb field there is a resident hare who lies in wait for us. It gets up just as we get to it and then me and Brain Dead take off after it. Fish has long since realised that her short stubby little legs will never get her anywhere near the beast. Today we got a great hunt all the way to the banks and down to the river where we always seem to lose it. Needless to say They yelled and whistled for us which we ignored. I had to follow Brain Dead back to the farm because I am not too familiar with the topography yet and I rather hoped she would delve deep into the recesses of what she claims to be a mind and remember the way home. In the end He did one of His ear cracking whistles. We caught up with them seconds before He would have had a stroke.

## April 5th

Today He arrived in the yard with the roof of the car covered with 8 foot posts and a whole lot of rails. It's not too surprising that the poor old car is ageing even faster than Him. He got His surveyors tape out and marked out the places for the rose border trellis which is about to spring up. Then we sat back and watched the pantomime that was bound to unfold. Well what with duff eyesight and wrecked shoulders from horse related accidents it was a miracle that He didn't bean Sid with the post basher while she courageously held the posts. On the whole He hit the posts more or less straight and she was uninjured. Then came the nailing of the cross

46

rails. Well, since arthritis struck His hands He is even more incompetent with a hammer. The chain saw got quite a bit of attention and there are some strange angles. All He could say was "Wait till the roses grow over it all-you'll never see the timberwork." Back in the sixties one of His work friends designed one of the bridges on the M1 just a few inches too short-that says it all really.

## April 8th

Sid ordered heaven knows how many roses from David Austin and planted them against the uprights. By the look of both Sid and Him they will both be dead before anything much covers the timberwork. I came out to have a good sniff round and had a great time christening each and every pole. He stood back to admire His work and has christened the whole ghastly edifice " ThorntonWood Henge". Of course He didn't bother to get the bottom lawn drained and it looks as if they might have hit a spring. He may have to have to invent a new game of "water croquet".

## June 14th

They have been advertising for a new tenant for the cottage and I detected a shimmer of anxiety in Sid's face when a rather smart single blonde turned up. There was an almost audible sigh of relief when it turned out to be the letting agent. Apparently when He went into the Estate Agent's office He managed to send all their business cards flying without really doing anything very much. His second wife banned Him from vulnerable shops unless His hands were in His pockets because it was becoming prohibitively expensive in breakages. Sid thinks she was right and has enforced the same rule in Northumberland. It is surprising how many things seem to fall to bits when He is anywhere near them.

The good news is that they have found a family with two youngish children and more to the point a splendidly bouncy dog called Bobby. Bobby is anthracite grey with an impossibly curly tail. He is a good deal bigger than me. But he has a smiley face and permanently looks pleased to be alive. It turns out that he is Italian and became part of their family by self-adoption when they lived in Italy. We think Bobby stowed away in their tatty yellow van when they came back to England.

His Father once lived in Italy along with one of his many wives and He used to go there quite a bit to visit them. On the strength of that He thinks He can converse with Bobby in his own tongue but in reality (which is a condition He isn't over familiar with) His repertoire is limited to yelling "chow" at the poor dog who looks unimpressed it has to be said.

Bobby still has all his bits, and horror of horrors MF fancies Him. Typical Italian. I bet he has an amazing repertoire of chat up barks. It is also rumoured that he is a sheep chaser so it's a bit baffling why they allow such a person onto what is predominantly a sheep farm. Just reinforces our opinion that most of their actions are completely incomprehensible.

### June 21st

Sid is banning Him from country shows. He has asked another man He met at another local show to build Him a summerhouse but to His specific design. Alan-the-shed as He calls him on account of the fact that He can never remember anyone's name has done a wonderful building. It is magnificent and cost almost twice what He was expecting. It is already full of junk but He's talking about having electricity put into it to power a small fridge: it wouldn't take a genius to work out what for.

My Mum is in a certain condition and keeps sneaking off to see Bobby. He gets frantic and rushes round trying to find her. I'm not sure I fancy Anglo-Italian half siblings. I like Bobby but I don't want him as a relative. They let Bobby off the lead today and after a fumbling attempt to get at Fish he legged it across the farm and was last seen on Ian's farm to the West. I think His heart is in the right place because He got quite anxious for Bobby's safety and took off in His car to try to find Him. Sure enough Bobby came nonchalantly out of a garden in the neighbouring village wagging his very continental tail and hopped into His car as if he was catching a taxi. Needless to say Bobby's family were very pleased to see Him back and me and Fish had a sneaking admiration for the young lothario.

### June 26th

We all went fishing to the Coquet today. We pottered around a field full of ewes and lambs while Sid and Him messed about with their rods. All they caught were tiddlers which didn't seem to bother Sid. I sensed however that He rather lost heart after a time and He pottered off to fish off the Priory wall which is a good 12 feet from the river level. Suddenly there was a terrific yell from Him. Sid legged it over the suspension bridge with me and MF wobbling over it behind her. There to our amazement was Him hopping up and down beside the Priory wall yelling "get on with it – I'm into a salmon you've got to net it for me". There are some tricky little steps set into the wall down which you have to go with fish on the end of your line in one hand and a net in the other. In other words more or less impossible unless you are a good deal more sprightly than He is. So poor Sid had to scale down the wall with the net to scoop up the luckless salmon. Once on land MF had to give it a good licking while I was quite happy to view it from a distance. It certainly looked bigger than any other fish I had seen Him catch.

Well He had to have His photograph taken with it and had to show it off to Hugh who weighed it at 8lb. Then it was necessary to open a bottle of bubbly. More photographs had to be taken and there was a lot of jollity.

## June 28th

Today He and Hurry up James have been building a pheasant holding pen in one of the small woods on the west side of the farm. First of all they had to assemble the materials. Posts from a local sawmill, netting and staples from Robson & Cowan, who He calls the Harrods of the North. All this stuff jammed into the back of the Mercedes with the posts lashed to the roof. Poor old car groaned its way across the fields where it visibly sighed as the stuff was removed. Of course He, who has never built anything before and certainly not a pheasant pen, decided to have a special gate which would stop the pheasants escaping.

The gate is based on the gull-wing door design for a 1950's Mercedes sports car. It doesn't work. If you have a bag of feed in one hand and water in the other you can't hold the gate open. It will fall back onto His head and He will curse and drop some thing. Hurry-Up James described to Andy Cowan this new venture as "another of my father's hair brained schemes". At the end of a long hard day's work the pen was ready. Everyone who is stupid enough to ask Him about it, and lots who don't, get carted out there to admire the thing. He's disproportionately proud of what is really no more than a chicken run. He smiles and pats it and it's all rather embarrassing.

We got dragged out there to inspect the edifice. It seems pointless to show a couple of JRs something they won't be allowed closer to than a few hundred yards once it is occupied.

## July 10th

The pheasant poults arrived today. He bought them from one of our neighbours. The game keeper Dennis brought them over and He and Dennis put them in with care – Dennis had a quirky smile, as if he knew something but wasn't going to tell. He of course, was all bushy tailed about it and kept counting to make sure that all fifty were there. When they had finished He stood back and admired the whole arrangement as if it had never been done before.

## July 11th

Well perhaps it wasn't the best thing to do. He took MF and me to admire His pen and its contents. We admired the contents at a smartish pace – round and round the pen. He got apoplectic as the poults panicked and tried out their pupative wings with no obvious success. Anyhow MF and I realised that we had better stop before He really did have that stroke. One of the poults had taken to lying on the ground on its side flapping in a rather helpless way. He navigated the gull-wing door, retrieved the hapless bird and we trudged off to the farm. We kept quite a low profile. In the kitchen Sid was set to work to revive what we were pretty sure was a pointless task. He kept saying "At £3.50 each we can't afford to lose any of them!" The whole thing baffles me since you can buy a brace of fully fattened pheasants oven ready from a butcher's for not much more than He paid for each of these.

The bird died.

## July 12th

Dennis came to see Him today to see how the poults were. It seems He's forgotten to build the "pop Hole" into the perimeter fence. If the truth is known He'd never heard of a "pop hole" so He legged it to Dennis' nearest pen – less than a mile away – and copied it. Needless to say He didn't get it quite right. Birds could get out but not back. I don't believe that that is quite what was intended. We weren't allowed to watch the redesign work but He came back to the farm looking pleased with himself and had to tell Sid all about it as if He had invented something for which the least reward would be a Nobel Prize.

## August 1st

Because we aren't allowed near the pheasant pen we are confined to West Moor Wood for our walks. Well today while inspecting all our usual rabbit spots there we flushed out a great bunch of his pheasant poults which had escaped. They can now just fly. Trouble is they aren't very expert at it yet and one of them garrotted itself on the fence on its way out. Once again there was a lot of yelling which MF and I didn't quite hear too clearly for a time until the veins on His neck began to throb too visibly. We stopped then because He's not much use to us dead.

He picked up the dead bird muttering "only forty-eight to go". We were sent back to the farm with Sid and He gently walked the troop of escapees back to the pen, a couple of fields away.

## September 14th

He came back to the house after feeding His precious pheasants looking completely baffled. It seems that when He got to the pen the pheasants had been replaced by two rabbits and a hedgehog. There wasn't a single pheasant to be seen anywhere. They had evaporated – He'd walked round all the woods and could find no sign of any of them. After His phase of bafflement He began to get cross then fortunately the funny side of the whole thing hit Him so He fired off one of His jokey letters to our next door neighbour from whom He bought the pheasants in the first place. He has accused them of selling Him "homing pheasants". The enigmatic smile on Dennis's face began to make sense.

## December 6th

Today was the great shoot. His friend Jim came to help beat with his dog Jack. I'm not allowed to help because He thinks I'm too manic ("pot calling the kettle …") and Brain dead wouldn't know why she was there. MF and Nearly Dead are gun shy so they hid in the darkest spider infested corner of the kitchen.

He looked overdressed in His tweeds. The boys, wearing jeans and woolly hats, had a couple of friends to help them fill the air with lead. He was carrying the four-ten which I suppose is just better than if He had a pocket of pebbles to chuck at the birds.

Well what a fiasco. He had worked out a sort of choreography which Hurry-up-James instantly tried to rewrite which annoyed Him. He even had a little map which no one could read or understand. Having put feed down in one or two strategic woods on the farm He had managed to entice just a few birds back onto the place. Quite a lot by our standards came out of Fox Earth Wood ahead of Jack whose daft tail looks like it will drop off from excitement. They missed the lot. Lots come out of the Clumps. They all flew on, quite unscathed, to Angus Wood. Now, Angus Wood is knee deep in impenetrable brambles but Jack found all the hiding birds which flew in perfect formation over the guns. One was shot. And so it went on. At the end of the day Ely did all right – three pheasants and three partridges was the bag. Poor Jack was worn out and disappointed. Still they had a good late lunch and a lot of laughs. Rob, who had never used a shotgun before was the most successful shooter. Big Nick had spent all his more adult years going to posh shoots about the place scored a duck. Hurry-up-James is the most blood thirsty member of the family and even managed to miss a lethargic rook that flapped lazily about the pond field just ahead of him.

## May 21st

He has decided to institute an inter village cricket match which is hardly ground breaking. He has challenged the next door village.
In the olden days they used to play a game of hockey on a flattish field near the house on Boxing Day every year. This was before our time but apparently He used to umpire the match which was taking quite a risk of a heart attack given the excesses of the season and His age even then. Anyhow part of what they used to call the Four Acre field has been taped off.

Sid bought an enormous tractor mounted mower while He was away in Dorset. It has never had a use but attached to their 40 year old Ford tractor makes a passably good cricket pitch mower. This machine makes hideous sounds and we confidently expect everything to fall to bits soon or the old Ford tractor to blow up. He trundled round getting out from time to time to view the effect. The horses looked on in amazement and Bess, His hunter, galloped off to the far end of the field because, along with just about everything, she is terrified of tractors. A handy sort of horse on a farm.

## June 25th

Disaster has struck. Today He tried mowing the pitch again but stopped more or less straight away. He came in to fetch Sid and we all had to go to investigate. It seems that a swallow has built her nest on a ledge in what is euphemistically called the cab. The nest contained four warm eggs. Sid is a bit of an expert on wildlife having done something on the subject at Durham University. The consensus was that it will be fine so long as He doesn't bounce over the ruts too fast. I have to say that the field is looking quite neat and tidy which is a bit unusual for this farm.

After lunch He went to the sports shop in Morpeth and bought mountains of equipment for the cricket match. The table in the "futility" room is now groaning under the weight of bats, pads, stumps and several balls. He even remembered a score book rather hoping that someone would remember how to fill it in.

## June 28th

He is becoming a bit obsessive about the pitch. Sid is getting bored by the daily bulletins on the subject. He has been filling in some of the deepest potholes caused by the horses because He fears a claim for injury should someone fall over. It doesn't seem to worry Him that someone might get killed crashing over one of His tatty old hunt jumps on the farm while hunting. I find His thought processes baffling. Perhaps the most bizarre thing is that the wretched swallows have hatched and we now have a tractor cab ledge full of tiny birds. The parents scream around the barn whenever He tries to get in. Sid says He shouldn't disturb them so believe it or not He is now mowing the two acres of pitch with the small garden lawn mower. There is a lane passing the field. Passers-by have taken to slowing down as they see this pantomime of an ageing lunatic mowing a field with a small Honda garden mower. It is becoming a spectator sport. We rather expect Him to start charging them.

## June 30th

The great day of the cricket match has arrived. He has set the scene quite well I suppose. His lorry, acting as the changing room though I don't think anyone had anything to change into or out of, is set on the boundary. It also houses the inevitable bar. Next to it is His little gazebo containing the scorer's table. He has vandalised one of the lorry partitions, painted it with blackboard paint and screwed it to the side of the lorry as a scoreboard. It seems that Hurry-up-James was official scorer at his secondary school so was ideal for the job. It's a bit of a lottery to see if he turns up on time. Straw bales have been sprinkled about as seating and eventually people began to trickle in.

He has been so preoccupied with this event that He has rather forgotten us but we get our daily exercise by following Him about while He prepares everything.

Sid has found, amongst her grandfather's things, a tiny silver cup, an almost exact replica of the FA cup. It is to be presented to the winning team. Adrian, the captain of the opposition, arrived without a team. It seems that they have been delayed in the Ox Inn so he had to return to extricate them. Unfortunately he had lost count of the number of people from the pub that he had asked to play with the result that thirteen people including his Sister-in-Law eventually turned up. In due course the two teams assembled in a variety of dress with the Rector and his two sons the only people properly attired. Fish is so besotted with Him that she had to be beside Him at His square leg umpiring position until she could see food or a child that she could molest. She finds small children irresistible because their faces are usually covered in sticky sweet leftovers so they get a good washing from her. Some parents regard it as a free valeting service; some don't.

His team won but only because, unknown to Him, one of His players was semi-professional and kept hitting the ball into the adjacent wildflower paddock where it got lost. It was just as well that He had bought several replacement balls.

At the end of the day we all retired to the dining room where refreshments including the inevitable alcohol were served and the Vicar presented Him with a bottle of whisky. No one quite knew why. It all got jolly and we polished off the leftovers. He looked smug because it all went off quite well and it didn't rain.

## August 10th

Since His return from Dorset one of His projects is to plant hedges all over the place as well as repair the old worn out fences. He says He wants the hedges up before He dies; hence the urgency. It's all these urgent projects that have got poor Sid on medication. There are endless frustrating delays trying to get Michael to the farm. Michael and his merry men have been planting trees and fencing on the farm for years. The problem is Michael also works for the Duke and inevitably The Duke gets first bite at this cherry. Quite frustrating though-the Duke is a good ten years younger than Him so has more time on his hands so to speak.

We get on famously with Michael because he arrives in a huge four wheel drive pickup smothered in fencing materials but best of all the men, unless the weather is unusually warm, have their meals in the cab. Fencers are notoriously untidy with their food and there is plenty to hoover up in there. MF is convinced that the world was invented for her comfort and convenience so a cab full of left-over lunch boxes and penguin wrappers is just the ticket. I followed her at a discreet distance being less self confident. Mind you she is usually right. In a way she has been a good Mother judging by the experiences she has passed on to me.

## August 15th

We went down to the river today. He took His little poacher's rod with Him. The size of the rod rather suggests He hasn't had permission to fish there. I don't want to be an accessory. Anyway at this time of year there's not a lot of water in the river so He hasn't got much of a chance of catching wily little northern brown trout.

MF plunged in as usual which scattered any fish that might be in some of the bigger pools. He didn't say much. She is so spoilt and indulged by Him. No one else would get away with it. There is a shelf of outcrop rock over which the depleted river runs in a shallow trickle. I teetered over it to the other side where I know there are rats living near a village sewer outfall. There is a road not far away and I find it quite gratifying that He gets anxious about me going near it and endlessly calls for me to return. If He only knew it I get a bit anxious when I am too far away from Him so I am not going to risk the road. Of course if a rabbit legged it in that direction I might not be able to resist.

Oddly enough He did get into quite a decent sized trout but lost it in the excitement and He got really quite excited when He thought He had seen an otter but subsequently decided that it was probably a mink. I expect He should be on some kind of calming substance.

## August 21st

We went to their place in Worcestershire where we go now and then for no obvious reason. All four of us were bundled into the now aged Mercedes along with food, Fishing rods and more coats than two people could possibly need. I suppose that the fishing rods were a bit of a clue as to the reason for the journey. We have been submitted to five hours monotonous Radio 4 and the M6. It was an uneventful journey except when He began to nod off and Sid had to take over. She hates the car – she calls it "Gopping Pink" while He maintains that it is "Cerise Red". She can't cope with the automatic gears. She is forever trying to change gear with excruciating results. That brings Him back to life pretty smartly.

When we got to the house we tumbled out. Then we saw that the lawn was covered with rabbits. They were well exercised by the time He and Sid had managed to round us all up. There is an orchard at the back of the garden. This slopes up to a large arable field. At the junction of the two there is a rabbit warren. I usually aim for that battle ground soon after we get there. He got very excited because the arable field is so big that if I really got going after one it could be hours before I reappeared. I find it quite gratifying that He should be so concerned.

## August 23rd

I'm sure He needs spare part surgery. They took us to a National Trust property called Brockhampton for a walk today. We three leapt out of the car in the car park and went our separate ways. Brain Dead disappeared in to a churchyard and suddenly set up a racket which indicated something interesting so MF and I went to join in. Well we found Brain Dead attached to one corner of a muntjac deer. MF and I latched on to a couple of other corners at which point the wretched thing started to make a fearful row. He suddenly appeared moving faster than I've seen Him move for some time, grabbed the deer and yelled at Sid to get us off. Sid had trouble getting the leads on us – all teeth and snarls (us not her) and then He said "My - - back has gone – I'm in agony – get on with it!" and then a lot of bad words. In the end we got hauled off and the Muntjac limped off into the shrubbery and He limped off back to the car. So that was the end of Brockhampton for the day.

They decided to go somewhere else for our walk so, all bloodied up, we got back into the car. What a fuss He made about His back. Far more than when He fell off His horse. He tottered about and after a not very satisfactory walk we went to His favorite local pub The Talbot where Sid fussed over Him and the landlord chided Him for not killing the Muntjac so that they could put it on their menu. I don't think He is very happy with the way today panned out.

**August 24th**

His back is better. We went back to Brockhampton. There are stacks of fallen timber in the park amongst which sporting rabbits hide. However there was no sign of the Muntjac hobbling about so me and MF got in amongst the fallen trees. Now and then we bolted one to another adjacent stack which is amazing fun. Well of course today Brain Dead joined in but her spindly, elegant legs can't stand the violent changes in

*Brain Dead under a blanket*

direction that rabbit chasing needs so surprise, surprise she ended up on three legs. He took no notice as usual. I bet it would have been a different story if it had been MF. Every one else has to be clinging onto life by a finger nail before He takes any notice. He, rather pompously, claims that His mother never took any notice of His ailments and that's what has made Him the stoic He is. Sid looked a bit more anxious. He insists on going the long way round which means a good old haul up and down some steep hills. We drew every covert for the four miles the Trust claims is the distance. There are masses of rabbits but we haven't seen any more deer.

Poor Brain Dead is really rather bashed up. When she goes to bed she burrows under her blankets and hides from the world. She's very strange.

### August 27th

We came back to the farm today. Brain Dead's hock has swollen up a lot and she isn't using that leg at all. Sid looked anxious and has arranged an appointment with the vet for the morning.

Although it is nice to go to the cottage it is nice to be reacquainted with the aga, our own vermin and the smells and comforts of home.

### August 28th

Brain Dead went to see Francis at the vets this morning. It seems that the leg is broken. It is now in plaster with a ridiculous pink bandage covering it up. We tease her about it but she is rather enjoying the attention. Needless to say He is unsympathetic. He said that she was jolly lucky that she wasn't a horse. I don't think that was very charitable and put it down to a feeble attempt at a joke. MF says that most of His jokes are not, on the whole, very funny and the rest are incomprehensible.

We went for a walk to the wood. Brain Dead came on a lead as Sid is anxious that she doesn't strain the plaster, presumably! I have to say that little MF is nothing like as much fun as Brain Dead for chasing things. Her legs are too short and I suspect she is getting a bit old and lazy. Also she is so besotted with Him that anything that takes her away from Him is not good. I suspect that if one could persuade Him to take up chasing rabbits she would join in with gusto. But I don't think He would last long.

**September 7th**

Today we were walking through our wood close to James's farm. We put up a couple of His precious pheasants and a partridge. They legged it onto James's farm pretty smartly. He was apoplectic.

Brain Dead has had the plaster taken off. She's quite perky now and enjoying the freedom. Sid kept the poor thing on a lead which we all find frustrating because we are used to hunting as a pack as it were.

He embarrassed us all this afternoon by writing to James to ask for His pheasants and partridge back. We are not certain whether He was serious. James's wife Emily had to give a reference for Him recently and she described Him as " Mad but harmless". Having spent a good few years away some of the locals are beginning to think that the warmer climate of Dorset probably softened His brain.

**October 8th**

It's His birthday again and He has two of His girlfriends from Dorset staying. I don't know how He has the nerve. Sid is jolly good about it. She sails through it all popping her Lisinopril and cooking wonderful meals. He took us all to Alnwick gardens for a treat which wasn't much fun for us because we aren't allowed in but the journey makes a change. Nikki is wonderful with us and makes a big fuss. I know Tess likes MF because on the whole she is placid but I get the feeling she is a bit wary of me. If the truth is known I'm not as punchy as people think. I'm not as good as my Mum at being teased, that's all. He says I take myself too seriously. It's as well people don't take Him too seriously or He would have been committed long ago.

The whole visit cost Him a bomb. Entrance for four adults is not cheap and He found a parking ticket on the car when they got back. MF and I did our best to intimidate the grumpy old man who had the nerve to stick the ticket on the windscreen while we were in the car but he was just indifferently rude back. Indifference is not something I am used to or will tolerate. When they got back to the car He tried not to look too upset but He's no actor.

## November 8th

He's hunting again. This time He has Mad Jane to help Him look after just one horse. He will claim that He is too old to look after a horse but if the truth is known He has never been without someone to help Him and sometimes more than one! And what's more He has never had more than four of the brutes at any one time. I call it shameful. Actually I think that the horses are quite lucky. He would get it all wrong so it's much better that they get professional help.

Mad Jane is tall and quite young. Her hair changes colour with the phases of the moon. I think she quite likes working for Him because He panders to her craving for Vodka. She has three dogs of her own and is wonderful with us. We can do no wrong so we get in amongst her long legs and generally help out in the stables.

Sid has been waging war on rats because one got into the roof or wall of the "futility" room. It was discourteous enough to die there setting up the most horrendous stink. It doesn't seem to bother Him so much. He says it will go away one day. He is philosophical like that sometimes. If there weren't a few rats about the whole place could be a bit short of excitement. Bess tends to drop bits of her feed sometimes and these are worth hoovering up.

Anyhow Mad Jane has a boyfriend called Fat Git who when he isn't working keeps her company with the Vodka bottle. They both have a passion for Newcastle United Football Club. Now and then when they have a party here He settles Mad Jane and Fat Git down with a bottle between them and they keep a pretty continuous supply of party eats coming our way.

## November 12th

Neighbour James seems to have forgiven Him the pheasant letter episode. There is to be a Christmas bazaar in James's walled garden at which He has been invited to sell MF's book "The Journal of Mortimer Fish." He took us down there to set up His stall. He had displays of photocopied, carefully edited letters from famous people who had written appreciative letters to Him about it. We all thoroughly enjoyed the day because lots of people came to see us and some even bought the book. Also there were food stalls and Sid kept bringing us samples. He enjoyed it mainly because the adjacent stall was selling His second favourite commodity, chocolate. The chocolatier was a more than usually beautiful girl. He spent a lot of money at her stall and practised His frankly cheesy chat up lines with her. She looked well up to dealing with that. Never mind it keeps His fantasies up and running.

**January 17th**

Sid says He's got ants in his pants. I'm not at all sure she should refer to his undergarments in public, and certainly there should be no reference to what we may or may not find in them. Anyhow it seems that if those ants are there they are on the move again because he's rushing about the place with a steel tape and a clipboard. It seems that He's got another building project in mind. What's the betting He falls foul of the planners again. It's amazing how he talks Himself out of trouble. Sid hides in the vegetable garden when the compliance officer, who is becoming quite a regular visitor, comes to see the latest carbuncle.

A rather harassed looking architect came to see Him. They kept up a pretty good pace walking round the house almost at the trot while He explained what He had in mind. After a time the architect began to look decidedly tired. It seems that He has in mind quite a major project. He got round to telling Sid after the architect had left. She looked more than usually manic at the prospect. She says that when it happens she is taking a few months off in Worcestershire or New Zealand with her cousins or just about anywhere that isn't here. He just nodded and put some finishing touches to His scruffy sketches.

**March 10th**

I don't quite know what got into me today. Soon after we got up I took to rushing round the breakfast room without touching the floor. It is decent of them to arrange the furniture in such a way as to make this sort of fun possible. After a bit and the scattering of some glossy magazines that were once on a little round table I calmed down in time for them to gather us up for a visit to Lowther in the Lake District. It seems that one of Sid's relatives has left her a dolls house that has been in her family for a good long time. The purpose of the journey was to pick it up. We chose one of the wettest days of the year to collect it. What they also failed to realize was that it is the Lowther Horse trials today so the whole area was locked solid with traffic. Well after the strange start to the day we had scant time to deal with our basic needs before we left and He was expecting to take us for a pit stop walk when we got there. By the time we arrived we were all getting pretty desperate. While Sid went into the house He took us for a drenching walk which was barely long enough to do the business. In the event the dolls house is quite small and rather battered. That suggests that a lot of children have enjoyed it. He of course has grand designs for enlarging it by adding a stable block at the back. Before long it wont fit into our farmhouse and will need a shed of its own.

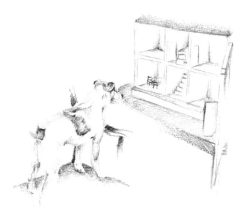

David from the village rang Him up today to say that there is a quantity of railway line for sale. It's another of His more than usually bizarre ideas. David has a small steam train which would fit onto this track. In anticipation of His inability one day to walk to His beloved wood He thought He might fix up a little railway line to and around it with a little engine shed near the farm. Sid began to look panicky when she heard about it. I don't think He has thought it through. The field is not exactly flat. Will there be cuttings and viaducts and level crossings or underpasses for the sheep and cattle? I wonder where that idea will end up.

**April 3rd**

My Mother has developed hay fever – she totters about the place sneezing. She screws up her hairy little face closes her eyes and positively explodes. He told her not to sneeze so loudly because at her age she might blow her little teeth out. She looked at Him witheringly. Sometimes her eyes are very watery so I try to dry them by licking them. He was anxious enough to take her to the vet who prescribed Piriton. She told Him that it was much cheaper from the chemist than from them. That was very decent of her and it pleased Him no end. Sid puts drops in MF's eyes too. It should be noted that none of it stops MF going down dusty old molehills or digging in rabbit holes.

After lunch some men came to prune a tree in the back garden to stop it interfering with the main electric line into the house. When He met them He told them to chop "the whole bloody thing down!" So they did – in the twinkling of an eye – He wandered around smiling that unnerving smile. It has to be said that the kitchen garden can now be seen from the kitchen window. It has inspired Him to design new, wider borders which will lead to a buying spree for cottage garden plants. Sid looked on from the safe haven of the "futility" room. She's the one who will have to plant them. All he does is rush off to Claire's nursery in the next village fill the boot of the car with plants leaving the rest to poor Sid. It's lucky that she has her tablets.

## April 16th

He's been out with the steel tape again. This time the front gates. Then He sat down in the breakfast room and started sketching new gates. As might be imagined His drawings were pretty extravagant and He gave them to "Rob the chippy" as He calls him. Rob corrects Him by calling himself a joiner. The pound signs in Robert's eyes lit up when he saw His plans. He's heard two things recently on Radio 4. One was an old, very old, Scottish doctor who attributes his longevity to porridge made with full fat milk and some fruit for breakfast and a healthy intake of whisky. This made Him very pleased. He is now planning for a long old age because He reckons that He has got the recipe right – God help us all! Poor Sid. The other thing was from another doctor – it amazes me that he listens to doctors bearing in mind His distrust of those He meets – to the effect that if you keep busy you will keep fit. I think this ties in neatly with His "ants". Anyhow there is no let up in the porridge and full fat milk intake and a day doesn't go by without Him being busy. It doesn't matter who is staying He goes to bed early saying "I'll turn into a pumpkin if I don't go up now" and off he goes. Poor Sid is left entertaining, filling the dishwasher and so on. By the time she gets to bed He's snoring with his glasses on the end of his nose and a book on his chest. We aren't sure if he ever reads a book.

## May 12th

We were going to the coast for a walk - just Him, Fish and me. On the outskirts of Morpeth the car began to wander all over the road. For a moment or two we thought that He was having the long awaited stroke. We could see a lay-by up ahead so He aimed for that without much confidence that He would get the car into it. When we did it was partly occupied by a large police car containing a large policeman. Fortunately He didn't hit it. Undaunted He got out and told the policeman that the steering had "gone funny" and could He borrow the policeman's phone to get His Daughter in Law to fetch us and then phone the RAC. I suppose He regards the police as public servants and here was one who could provide Him with a bit of service. The policeman looked slightly surprised but the confidence of the old man was such that it seemed a reasonable request.

Eventually Hurry up James's wife turned up at just about the same time as the RAC man. The Policeman had done a bunk fearing, no doubt, a request for a take-away or something in that line.

Anyway He sent Anita home because the RAC man said that it was just the suspension and it would go on for hundreds of miles. We turned round and headed back home. Well the road between Morpeth and the farm was clearly surveyed by a man in a bad state of inebriation. Just about as soon as you have taken a sharp left a sharp right pops up. The car did some very strange things. Once or twice He was not sure on which side of an oncoming car we would pass it. We struggled home and He really did look pretty rattled. For the first time in my life I really worried about Him.
It turned out that whatever keeps the back wheels parallel had given up the ghost so that whatever direction the front went was not necessarily the direction taken by the back wheels. A low loader came to take the car away.

## May 20th

Nick got married to his very nice little Irish girlfriend. Needless to say the event took place in Ireland. Sadly we weren't allowed to go but apparently He excelled Himself by inviting two of His Dorset girlfriends as well as His glamorous step daughter and hired a biggish car so that the whole harem could go together. The Dorset lot all flew to Belfast and Sid, He and

Geors flew from Edinburgh meeting up with Tess and The Lovely Kate at Belfast. Then ensued several days of revelry during which He behaved pretty badly on the whole. His car got a puncture; He couldn't figure out the hand braking system so nearly reversed into the wedding car. What's more He forgot to wear His nifty little grey waistcoat for the ceremony so that His belly stuck out. The last event, He claims, was caused by the fact that everyone had to change in the same room in the huge hotel so try as He might He simply couldn't concentrate. At the reception He managed to find an Irish relative of the bride's family to talk hunting to and was offered a "splendid forward going" hunter for a day or two. He looked slightly scared and backed off a bit! The hotel had a spa complex which included all sorts of watery pursuits and on the last day He couldn't get His harem out of the water to go to the airport. Eventually they made it and we were mighty glad to see them all back, even if He did look a bit as if someone had pole-axed Him.

**August 17th**

Hurry-up-James's wife is heavily pregnant with their third child which He regards as at least one too many. Today is Hurry-up-James's birthday. We all know He has a bizarre sense of humour so I suppose we shouldn't have been surprised by His present for the hapless man: A carefully wrapped box which contained what He described as a "Home Vasectomy Kit" consisting of a couple of nicely wrapped bricks and a set of instructions. He also made the comment that a rescue dog would have been much more eco-friendly than another "damn" child.

Fortunately Hurry up James found it all amusing as did his wife. He has framed the instructions apparently.

**September 2nd**

It has rained for thirty-six hours non-stop. Morpeth is under water because the river has burst its banks. Fortunately the farm is on a hill so I rather doubt if we will get flooded but it has transformed the fields. The one known as the pond field is now more like a lake. His friend Hugh says you can't claim to live in a "Gent's Res" unless you have a lake so now He reckons that they qualify.

There are rivers everywhere and the water is up to the top of the gate in the silage paddock. It's all very spectacular. It is supposed to be summer.

MF loves it because she's into swimming but I hate it and paddle about in misery. I tiptoe to the woods and He laughs at me which is a bit unkind really.

## October 12th

Many years ago He bought a Subaru estate car for His wife. It died recently at the hands of his stepdaughter Geors so he kept it on the farm as a runabout. It's now stuck in a flooded field. You'd have thought that by His age He'd have grown out of playing Land Rovers in the mud. I expect it will stay there until the floods recede. We go for great walks. MF is enjoying this weather. She dashes through the puddles immersing her furry little body. She looks like a bedraggled rat. He's not very polite about her anymore. I think that at one time He was a tiny bit scared of her. Now He gives her names like "Flee infested fur ball".

He's back to hunting on the brute Bess. It was His birthday this week and they had the hunt breakfast here to celebrate this great achievement. Not too surprisingly, He decided that the breakfast would go down well with a glass of Buck's Fizz so He lashed out on a very good deal at M & S and bought far more than was needed. They aren't all as addicted as He is but as He put it there will be plenty for next time. We had a great time cruising underneath the long tables set up in the barn, scooping up left over sausages, bacon and buns. The chickens, who usually roam free, were banned so we got the jackpot. He felt sorry for the ducks, who were also confined to their hutch and let them out. Four runner ducks strutting about the place like self-propelled umbrellas caused a lot of amusement. The breakfasters sang 'Happy Birthday' to Him and He pretended to be embarrassed.

I have to confess to hating foxhounds. They really do annoy me. I don't know what it is but I only have to see one in the distance and I begin to boil up. So to find about thirty of them here on the farm almost caused me apoplexy. MF doesn't seem to mind at all and Brain Dead is too dim to know how she feels about them or anything much, actually. If a foxhound comes near me I simply have to have a go at it. He says that it's quite embarrassing given His preferred hobby. Incidentally He has just about given up flying the silly little helicopter, which, He says is much too expensive now with petrol prices through the roof.

## October 21st

Poor Nearly Dead isn't well. She's given up eating and looks like she can't see very much or hear much either. Moreover she's got a nasty lump on her tummy. Sid's taking her to see Francis. He said He'd go too because it looks like it may be the end. Sure enough Nearly Dead is. They took her down to the wood and buried her near the wild cherries on the West Side. Sid planted some bulbs over the grave. She was a really nice companion and it has to be said that she was the only dog that has put up with me and MF without once complaining and readily gave up her bed if we wanted it. We'll miss her good-natured toothless grin but not the haddock breath.

I'm in trouble. Me and Brain Dead had a racing rumpus round the pond field and I got a bit over excited and bit her side. It's such thin skin that quite a big hole appeared. Sid got excited and He just gave that manic laugh which worries me just as much as it did my mother. I think Sid was hoping for more contrition on His part.

## November 10th

He's suddenly been affected by a new enthusiasm. In the past His carpentry skills were restricted to what you can do with a chain saw. Now He has bought Himself a couple of enormous do-it-yourself books and studies them at the breakfast room table. Sid looks on anxiously.

This afternoon He took us into one of the sheds, shut the door and began to try to make sense of the chaos in there. It used to be a feed room and to some extent still is. I gathered that our role was to chase and hopefully dispatch any rats that might come to light. As it happens there were plenty of rat smells and quite a lot of evidence of them. At one point He got agitated because rats had been into a plastic dustbin into which He had carelessly thrown a number of umbrellas rescued from His father's house when he died. I can't see why He makes a fuss about the now well perforated umbrellas because He has never been seen to use one. He said that one day He would shake the world and go to London and He'd need an umbrella then. I think He's been looking at archive footage of when He was a lad and everyone in London, so far as He could see, had bowlers and umbrellas. As He moved packing cases and boxes of rubbish so MF and I squeezed in behind or under them in a fever of excitement.

Hope certainly springs eternal but we didn't find anything killable. They don't taste good but the chase is the game. He cleared a space and then took off in the old Mercedes returning with an estate car crammed to the gills with heavy timber.

**November 12th**

He and Sid went off to B & Q today and returned with endless boxes of tools, gadgets, and boxes of screws. They had also bought a self-assembly cupboard from IKEA. That was a mistake. He had it all out on the concrete floor of the cattle shed and was going funny colours trying to work out what went where, how and why. If the truth is known it was pretty simple and the instructions, if He hadn't mislaid them early on, were quite good. Then Sid got involved. She did her school mistressy bit, which annoys Him because she's nearly always right and things plop into place for her. So He got grumpy and silent and she eventually reckoned that the house needed her attention and she made a strategic withdrawal. The cupboard got made but the door hinges resembled, to Him, something out of the space programme. They didn't do what they should have done and without a doubt it was the manufacturers at fault. Sid came to the rescue and He went off for a restorative whisky and to feed us. I have to say that whatever disaster befalls them He always feeds us at the same time every day. It all stops for our supper-we appreciate it and He worries about our diet.

**November 13th**

It seems He's decided to make a workbench which is a logical start I suppose. No one is confident that anything will be "worked on" on this bench but He is aiming high. However it is not some handy little thing but something to compliment Stonehenge. We don't get much in the way of walks when these enthusiasms are on Him.

He started on the big bits of wood, measuring them and trying to follow the instructions in the D.I.Y. book which He is rapidly coming to the conclusion were written by a barely educated Chinese person like the IKEA cupboard. It turned out that although He had given very detailed sizes of timber to the suppliers they had interpreted His notes in a liberal manner adding a good deal of imagination to the task.

He went funny colours again and packed all the timber up in His car and took it back to the suppliers something like twenty-five miles away. He told the manager that the timber had travelled fifty miles and hadn't been touched yet. Could the teenager who sawed it originally come out of his hangover and try again this time having some regard to the instructions. The child looked at the timber and at the instructions, did a bit of measuring and grumped off to his saw-bench, hitching his trousers up a fraction before they descended to the floor of the workshop.

This time the timber of roughly the right lengths and sizes was produced and reloaded into the car for the journey back from Tyneside. Some of the best-travelled bits of sawn timber in the world He muttered to us on His return.

## November 23rd

The workbench is completed. It is magnificent. It is monumental. It dwarfs everything including Him. His mother's old dining room table is a side table. Amongst other invaluable tools on this side table is His beloved digital radio and an elderly television. There are some shelves on a wall that have a hint of left hand down and an enormous notice board has been screwed to another wall onto which He intends to pin plans of projects. An old set of Avery scales decorate the third wall along with a Superser gas heater. It all begins to look quite cosy. Even wine racks have appeared. I'm not at all sure we'll see Him this winter.

He took us for a rather brief, damp walk to look at the floods in one of the fields. I would prefer it if He didn't. It is of no interest to me and the cosy bed beside the Aga is my preferred place.

*Me and my Mum*

## December 4th

A disastrous day. He took us Christmas shopping to Newcastle. His beloved Mercedes, which is 13 years old now, had to have a new head gasket last week because it was using more water than petrol. The repair was done. Then half way down the spiral ramp out of the multi-storey car park above John Lewis in Newcastle the engine stopped.

Fish and I were unaware of the drama except that He got quite agitated because without an engine He had no steering or brakes. It was not an ideal place to find one's self without power and in fairness to Him He did pretty well to find a slot to park in and stop without penetrating the retaining wall and precipitating us all into the bus station hundreds of feet below.

By some miracle He had His phone with Him, which is pretty unusual, so He could phone the RAC. The RAC man's van was too high for the ramp so by the time he did eventually turn up on foot over an hour later we were getting very cold. He had wrapped us up in His coat. I suppose we have to assume He is fond of us. The mechanic opened the bonnet poked about, did some rather intimate things to His beloved car and pronounced it dead of timing chain failure. Even He knew that that was pretty serious.

Now to give Him even more credit, and it worries me that He will get big headed if I go on in this vein, He rang Sid to come and fetch us so that we didn't get too cold during the next stage of this saga, waiting for the break-down van.

Just to illustrate what a bad idea it is to breakdown in that sort of place, the rescue van had to begin by pulling Him out backwards, up the spiral ramp in order to get the front of the car to point downwards, so to speak, first, then while He kept the traffic waiting it squeezed past Him, hitched onto the front end and towed Him down the spiral ramp and into rush hour traffic in Percy Street, through two sets of traffic lights and up a one way street the wrong way to the waiting low loader. All this in the dark! As He watched His beloved Mercedes ignominiously driven away it is reported that a tear or two ran down His cheek.

## December 10th

What a weekend. We sort of knew something was up because Him and Sid have spent a week buying up the local supermarket and then cooking for days on end. Anyhow the rot set in on Friday when Nick, wife and incontinent child, tipped up along with enough baby equipment to fill a transit van. Nick looked done-in just bringing all this stuff into the house and Molly, their miniature JR raced round in ever decreasing circles yapping. She doesn't do our cause any favours but the poor girl has got to advertise her existence since the pink blob made its appearance. He can't help with all the packing cases of baby equipment because of His damaged shoulders (three hunting accidents ago!). The bedrooms here are quite big but all that clobber makes them look totally inadequate. Erne (Nick's wife) is pretty keen on shoes, clothes and girly things in general so another fair sized van load was brought in for her.

They arrived late – after His suppertime anyway – and then the servicing of the tiny baby began at one end and progressed to the other. Then it all started again. I don't remember my mother having to service us quite so constantly. Eventually He got His supper a good two hours after He is used to getting it so He was quite grumpy. Me and MF love children so we did our best to clean up the child all over – some bits tasted better than others – but we were discouraged which was a shame. Anyhow the baby, or Pink Blob as He calls it, said nothing and did little more than gaze vacantly about it. Its eyes were open so it must be a few weeks old.

Eventually He shuffled off to bed before He turned into a pumpkin.

## December 11th

Hurry up James turned up with daughter, Katherine, Shrimpy (as He calls His younger granddaughter) and his extremely pregnant wife, who He refers to as Fatty – One day she will dot Him one. Again a largish amount of children's equipment came with them. I'm beginning to think that they need a team of porters for all this stuff. The house is getting smaller. I love Katherine and Shrimpy because they move independently of adults so we can chase them. They are suitably scared and run away squealing. On the whole He likes peace and quiet so the raised decibels in the house make Him look as if He is in a certain amount of pain so more whisky has to be administered to anaesthetise His hearing. Well that's what He says. Anyhow Hurry-up-James and his expanding family pitched their camp in another room.

Well just as everyone was settling down to a simple lunch another couple arrived with another minute baby looking exactly like a wrinkled prune with a hairy blunt bit. It also seemed to need constant attention to both polar regions. So what is all this? Something is afoot - not another of His parties I hope.

After lunch they tottered out for a go at the farm pheasant. Sid, two girl helpers and one of the guests were beaters along with a hairy German pointer. He was an ugly brute of a dog so I went for Him. They really don't need to be so big. I am living proof that size doesn't matter. The rest of them went off to the first drive. Quite a lot of birds came out – all are still flying about the place. After a couple of hours the tally was two more than had ever been shot here before. Everyone looked pleased and He looked smug because He had accounted for more than His usual tally. The German pointer went home after the shooting and not before time in my opinion. MF takes a more sanguine view.

I couldn't believe it when, later, six more people turned up but thankfully no more pink blobs. They weren't staying the night so didn't traipse through the place carrying packing cases of equipment or whatever. One of the next batch was a man from Eastern Europe so He took to gently teasing the poor fellow. Fortunately the man in question gave as good as he got. They had a noisy dinner party and as ever He had too much to drink, chatted-up a gormless blonde and went to bed early. It's amazing that anyone ever agrees to stay or eat here. It has to be said that the food is good; Sid is a brilliant cook. We know because we hover under the table like our medieval ancestors picking up all the leftovers.

## December 12th

They all got smartened up today and went off to church. Considering how He knocked it back last night He looked remarkably chirpy and I think it is the first time I have seen Him in a suit and tie. Needless to say it was not a very appropriate tie having been bought on a London railway station when He was in one of His less than serious moods prior to a meeting with His Father's "pompous lawyer." As He described him.

At church the vicar poured water over little Luke's lid which is a bizarre ritual I reckon. They needn't try it on me. After this bit of strange behaviour the whole lot including the vicar and his family came back for another mammoth blow out. A lot of baby worshiping got underway which He finds pretty irritating so He kept moving from room to room to avoid the worst excesses of cooing and billing.

As for us, we got forgotten but as food seemed the priority this weekend, if you ignore baby worshipping, we were fully occupied clearing up the inevitable droppings.

## December 20th

I've never seen so much drink in the house. The "futility" room is knee deep in cases of wine, bottles of whisky and so on. It looks like another of His parties is coming up. We had to be shut in the dining room while He ferried all the boxes and cases from the car. Poor car. It must feel like a brewer's dray sometimes. I think Bess is quite lucky that she hasn't been harnessed to a four wheel cart for the run to and from the booze shops in Morpeth. Sid has been hoovering and polishing. He rather irreverently describes it as "mucking the place out". He has a point however it has to be said that it is often Him who is seen wandering through the house in His wellies.

The Christmas tree is in the hall and the mistletoe He got from Worcestershire is hanging from the light fitting. I suppose He thinks He might relive a passionate moment or two. What a memory!

We get pretty short shrift in these circumstances too. They don't have much time for entertaining us. Since the really brief walks we get are not very inspiring we retire to our beds, keep our heads down and dream of peace and quiet and rabbits.

Nick and family including Molly are here again for Christmas with all their equipment. Sid and He mutter on about how in their day the babies had to make do with Mothercare carrycots which doubled up as push chairs with the addition of little wheels and everything was transported on the back seat of Sid's Mini. Molly kept up a more or less constant yapping which no one seemed to notice.

## December 22nd

I assume today is the day of their party. Furniture is getting moved round and glasses put on the kitchen table which also groans under the weight of bottles. People began to arrive at about the moment Fish, Me and Molly got shut in a bedroom. Heaven knows why. I'm quite sociable these days. He says I've mellowed. The usual forest of legs at these events often heralds the arrival at our level of some pretty tasty morsels but when the tide of people recedes and we are liberated there will be lots of hoovering up for us to do. When He was a bachelor in Dorset we reckoned that this was how he did His house work when Heather wasn't due.

After a time the noise levels really got pretty dreadful and you could tell that the place was heaving under the weight of vacuous chatter. One of His oldest (and they are beginning to get pretty ancient) friends and his son decided to wreck the dining room, which was an odd way to repay hospitality. It was all quite repairable but He, rather than getting cross, just looked mystified. I think He is mellowing too.

At one point He seemed to disappear and was found showing their pretty young neighbour, Helen, all His hunting and horsey pictures which are sprinkled round this rambling house. Needless to say there was a lot of intemperate giggling about etchings from some of the guests who knew Him all too well. Eventually, far too late so far as we were concerned, the last very drunken couple left. At this point we were sprung and could chase round the house hoovering. He subsided into an armchair stoked up a nice big whisky and watched the "young" as He calls them tidy up, fill the dishwasher and service "pink blob".

## December 23rd

His friend Jim turned up today all dolled up in shooting breeches for the annual formal teasing of the farm pheasant. Jim brought his lovely manic Spaniel, Jack who is employed to find the pheasant. We were shut away because He says I'm always in the wrong place and Fish is gun shy.

He has acquired walkie-talkies which sent Big Nick and Hurry-up-James into paroxysms of laughter. He spent ages in Comet getting the best one He could so was rather put out by this display of filial insobriety.

He assembled the troops, gave them a completely unnecessary talk on the choreography of the day and off they went. Bearing in mind that He put down fifty pheasants in August there seemed to be a bit of a dearth of birds. The first covert is where all the birds should be. Those very few that were there flew, perversely, in the wrong direction straight to Trevelyan country. However it has to be said that even if they had learnt to hover twenty feet above the guns they would have been safe. At about this moment one of the walkie-talkie's began to broadcast in a foreign language . He was baffled and abandoned the devices. By halfway through the day nothing had been shot. Luckily the penultimate wood yielded a few pheasants of which four were shot. Hurry-up-James has always had a blood thirsty streak in him but is consistently unable to shoot anything however hard he tries. It is a tradition that The Pond Wood which is really very small but which usually houses a few birds who like mud is reserved for Hurry-up-James. As ever he failed to shoot anything despite the apparent suicidal tendencies of the birds which flew out ahead of Jack.

The poor hapless birds that were unfortunate to get shot this year were laid out on the table in the "futility" room just out of our reach but very much within olfactory range. That's mean. Brain Dead is big enough to get one but hasn't yet worked out where the smell is coming from.

They then had a convivial lunch. We got to go to that which is great fun. He was so relieved that the whole charade was over for another year that He let His hair (what's left) down and took to teasing Jim who gave as good as he got.

## January 6th

He went hunting again on Saturday. It really is time that He realised that He is no longer the right age to be trying to do a whole day. The upshot is that He has a pain in His back. It is so bad that He's had to go to His new favourite masseuse Kate. Not only does she rub His decrepit old back but she sticks needles in all over the place. It seems that He enjoys it – which rather confirms my view that He's definitely peculiar. I suppose it might have something to do with the fact that Kate is tall and blonde. She is as mad as He is. When He came to get dressed again He found a needle still in His ankle. He gingerly pulled it out. When He told Kate all she said was "Oh! I often do that, I rather lose count of the number I have put in.

The other day I forgot one in someone's head and he only found it when he came to put his hat on!" After paying He asked her if it was OK to go hunting on Saturday. Kate rounded on Him saying "You are the maddest man I have ever treated!" And she pushed Him out.

It obviously did Him good because He took us for a longish walk back down to the river this after noon. On the way we found that sporting hare in the Bomb field again. Me and Brain Dead gave it a good run for its money. MF gave up after a few yards fully aware that she didn't have a hope. Brain Dead and I chased it round the plough quite a bit and then it went off into Jock's flat. We went on down to the river but on the way my foot began to hurt again. By the time we got back to the farm I was on three legs. He looked at me gloomily. He's not trying any of His remedies on me and He knows it so I expect He's thinking about the medical bills that might ensue.

## January 7th

Sure enough He took me to the vet today. Normally He would enjoy the visit because His favourite vet, Francis, was likely to be on duty. I spoil it a bit for Him because of my disinclination to allow anyone to mess about with my bits. It becomes a battle of who I can bite as they dodge my teeth. I get grumpy just at the sight of the table thing I am supposed to stand on while they poke and prod my intimate areas.

I didn't get a chance to bite anyone not even Him. After explaining the circumstances He told them to sedate me and do a proper job, whatever that means. I had no say in the matter – they drugged me, did things and then after a perfectly bloody day He sailed in all sweetness and light to collect me. It was almost as if I'd had a day at the seaside the way He behaved. I was quite grumpy. I didn't want Him to see that actually I was very pleased to see Him. Francis suggested that they put Vaseline on my wound – they only tried that once!

## January 12th

Today He had to go back to "Kate the needle" as He calls her. His back is still giving Him jip. He got a special early appointment before Kate's regulars got in.

After His session of being punctured all over the place He went back to the reception to be greeted by His hunting chum Emily who, being a good generation or two younger than Him, said "Oh! I see it's help the aged first here then!" Give Him His due He thought that was quite funny. He told Kate that He was going hunting on Tuesday. Again she shrieked at Him that He certainly is the maddest man she's ever met. At last someone's got His measure. We got a rather peremptory walk to the wood which now contains red squirrels which Sid is feeding in a special box thing. They both get a bit over-excited if we so much as look interested in the ginger critters.

## January 14th

Brain Dead has done it this time. They feed the manky old red squirrels hazel nuts. A whole nut must have been dropped by one of the clumsy little critters which Brain Dead then ingested. It got stuck in various bits of her gut as it tried to escape. She tried, unsuccessfully, to expel it by being sick and eventually she gave up eating altogether which is unheard of. So Sid took her to the vet where an x-ray showed the nut neatly tucked up in the middle somewhere. They got all her giblets out on the operating table and frisked them not only for the nut but anything else "foreign" while they were at it.

Sid sent Him to get Brain Dead and the vet, not appreciating His delicate feelings about matters medical, gave Him a blow by blow account of the procedure. He nearly fainted and had to exit pretty smartly before they had to treat Him too. Brain Dead now has a plastic cone on her head and has to be carried everywhere for fear of bursting her stiches. He keeps a discreet distance.

## January 18th

He has been trying to trace His family. If genetics are as important as they say I bet there are some murky bits in there that He might be well advised to leave alone. During the course of His searches He has discovered that a certain senior Liberal Democrat peer is His first cousin so Big Nick has taken to teasing Him about His " New Best Friend". However in His NBF's autobiography he describes His family as pretentious. He now makes rude noises if NBF is seen on television. A bit childish if you ask me.

**January 20th**

We went for a walk to the outer reaches of the farm this afternoon. He nearly had the long awaited stroke when we got to one of the "Clumps" as they are called. They are a series of little copses. The tenant's sheep were in it knocking back the young trees as fast as they could push over their plastic guards. We had a great time chasing the wretched things out and He ranted a good deal-probably to some extent because He realised that His fences were awful. After that we went to inspect His version of a Pheasant pen. He is determined that this year they will have a good crop of birds even if they are all such rotten shots-it's nice to have something to fire at as He puts it. Foxearth wood was lifting with rabbits so MF and I had a great time going underground while Brain Dead stood around vacantly wondering where we and the rabbits had gone. The rabbits in Foxearth aren't as sporting as those in West Moor wood. They at least get up and run a good few yards before finding sanctuary. After a time a big old rabbit shot out of a hole and Brain Dead took after it at summer lightening speed. She was so focussed on the rabbit that she failed to see the wire fence looming fast and ran smack into the wire. She's limping a good deal now. Sid won't be pleased. She pays BD's repair bills.

**January 23rd**

I knew that looking up His ancestors would be counter productive. It seems that three eminent politicians are in there each of them in a different party. The most celebrated was a Quaker mill owner from Rotherham who was almost certainly very left wing, erudite and an all-round good egg. If the truth be known I think He is most proud of him really but probably doesn't know where Rotherham is.

The new farm tenant, Ian, has a collie called Basil. Basil is lovely but suffers from a couple of disadvantages in his allotted task in life. Ian once ran over him with a bit of farm machinery reducing the poor dog to only three effective legs. Under normal circumstances four legs on a collie would seem pretty much the required number for the job so Basil shambles around enthusiastically but without a lot of success. His other problem, which is rather more serious, is that he is frightened of sheep. Today on our walk we watched Basil being chased across one of our fields by about fifty "Blackies" who take no nonsense from anyone much. They cornered him in a gateway which distressed poor Basil.

Years ago Ian's Father, Bill, had a collie which bit everyone including Ian's Father. You couldn't get out of the car without Muttly having a go at you. When Bill applied for a shot gun licence the local policeman

*Basil asleep on the quad*

came to inspect the arrangements and got the Muttly treatment as he emerged from his police car. After inspecting the arrangements in the house the policeman asked what other security arrangements were in force. Bill replied "You have just met him" which didn't go down at all well.

**January 24th**

He got all dolled up again in His shooting gear to go shooting with His chum James. He almost looked smart for a change because He has bought Himself a Gortex shooting coat. Unfortunately it is a good two sizes too big for Him and looks like a tweed dressing gown. He has had to turn up the cuffs and can only just reach the bottom of the zip. Normally He is in His moribund Barbour with a broken zip. The whole would have looked quite good if He had had some proper garters instead of which His shooting socks were kept up with household string which dangled below the turn ups and made Him look more than usually impecunious.

He came home with tales of missed birds and how Charlie fell into the snipe bog trying to push James's quad out of the mud. We reckoned that He had had one or two little drinkies because He was very bubbly and rather silly. Sid is amazingly good natured with Him. He once had such a hangover that the day after He chose bananas for breakfast because they were quieter than cornflakes.

**January 26th**

He told Sid that He needed a rest. A rest from what? Most people need a rest from Him. Anyhow MF and I were bundled into the old Mercedes along with endless coats, wellies and dog leads and we are now at the cottage in Worcestershire. We aren't too sure why we are but it suits us as we love it. It's a long drive but we two spend most of the time asleep rather hoping that He stays awake. He got quite excited seeing the snow on the Lake District hills and waxed lyrical about the scenery. To be honest scenery seems a bit pointless unless one can be in it chasing something. But we humoured Him by opening one eye from time to time to look at it.

Our first port of call was His beloved Waitrose in Malvern which He likes almost as much as the one in Salisbury. Out came the card and into the back of the car went enough bags of food to feed a small school for a whole term. I rather wonder how long we are here for. When we got to the cottage me and MF went rabbiting in the orchard where there is a huge bramble patch into and out of which rabbits scurry in a tantalising way. He gets excited because He can't see us and imagines we won't know the way home. He should know by now that a JR doesn't get lost that easily.

**January 27th**

He was pretty late getting down to us this morning which rather suggests that He didn't sleep too well which doesn't surprise me given the amount of supper He put away last night. We went for a long walk over the fields to the village and back but there weren't any rabbits and it was terribly muddy. When we got back we hopped into His car and He yelled about "filthy socks on His upholstery". I would have thought that it was a good deal too late to be worrying about that sort of thing given the disgusting state of the car in general. It's completely unsellable now anyway so what does it matter. Later on He managed to stall the wretched thing at some traffic lights in Malvern. He couldn't restart it. There was a road sweeper busy on the other side of the road so He called to him to push the car to the side of the street where we were less in the way. The man obliged looking slightly baffled. Far from being anxious about it we sat beside the kerb while He calmly ate a sandwich. After a few minutes He tried again and it started perfectly well. He and it are very unpredictable.

We trailed around Malvern trying to buy a radio for the cottage without success. Once again He dived into His beloved Waitrose for a bit of retail therapy. After that we were taken off to Worcester where He parked improperly and had an unresolved "discussion" about it with a lady parking meter attendant. He has a very long fuse so these "discussions" are usually good natured. He bought a sophisticated radio which He will never learn to use in a million years.

We had a nice but uneventful walk at Brockhampton this afternoon. I remembered the incident of the Muntjac deer and I went to the churchyard to see if it was still there. It wasn't.

## January 28th

He is in a bad mood. On the way to a new walking place He broke the sun visor fixing in His elderly car. We took no notice of the cursing; He'll get over it and lets face it rather more fundamental things have fallen off it before now. Sid once removed a door handle. Has He ever told you about when He reversed into a staircase in Sussex? He becomes evasive if asked why He was inside a house in the car.

We went to Bringsty Common. It is a sort of derelict landscape pock-marked with smallish houses and surprise, surprise a pub. We rootled about in the undergrowth but found absolutely nothing at all to chase. In the distance we saw three collie dogs. They are usually good for a couple of rounds and we started off after them but He called us back.

He had spied the pub. It looked His kind of place – not too smart and He is already working out a walk which might start in their car park and end in their bar. He was anxious to tell Sid about it on the phone and it transpires that the pub was at one time owned by her family brewery. As an historical note this part of Herefordshire is sprinkled with pubs that used to be owned by Sid's family but they sold the brewery not so long ago which causes Him no end of grief. Sid's Father used to take Him on a lot of tours of these places.

There was a famous occasion in one of their pubs when He was trying to impress her family before they were married. He started bragging about his knowledge of whiskies. In His absence for a moment or two the landlord who had been privy to the discussion substituted beer and water for His Teachers and He didn't notice to the merriment of all in the know. He has never again claimed expert knowledge of whisky.

He is packing up so I presume we are going back to the farm tomorrow. I do rather miss the aga.

**January 30th**

It's the last day of shooting because tomorrow is a Sunday so the whole countryside has erupted into a cacophony of gunfire. MF is terrified. We all went for a longish walk to the river again and I braved the cold water and went to look for rabbits amongst the drains. I love doing that because He gets gratifyingly anxious when I'm so near that road. MF plunged in and joined some boys who were playing with bows and arrows near the grotto.

He started looking for wild garlic – where is the sense in that – it's only January. I had a great time on the banks getting rabbits galore on the move I managed to rouse a couple of roe deer and me and Brain Dead chased them over the wheat field. Even I realised I couldn't hope to keep up and Sid called Brain Dead off because she is the only one of us

*Me gazing into the garden*

who could and we don't want another Muntjac episode.

They went out to dinner leaving us on our own for hours. They got back in the early hours by which time Brain Dead who is completely incontinent when she gets anxious about where Sid is and worrying about whether she will ever come back had disgraced herself all over the kitchen. She came from a broken home so we have to indulge her.

## February 8th

One of their friends has a few cows one of which got a problem with its giblets and had to be put down by the hunt. It was too good to feed to the hounds. I regard that as a bit insulting to canines. A great many people rely on the hounds to keep running all day for their entertainment so one would have thought that no food is too good for them. They brought the poor beast to the farm and strung it up in the big shed. They didn't tell us though and so when we went out for our early morning walk it looked for all the world like a rather oversized brown rabbit hanging from a beam by a back leg. At first we got quite excited and went for it but needless to say when it didn't respond we rather lost interest. As an amazing side note, first of all they tied the poor beast to some railings which formed a cattle feed trough concreted into a wall. On hoisting the animal the railings came out of the wall pulling part of the wall down with them. His only reaction on seeing the debris was to say "Good we needed some rubble to put in the gateways". After that they attached the rope to the Ford tractor which has been here since the world began. It didn't move so presumably the tractor is heavier than the cow. What worries me is whether the beam is strong enough. If not a rather large covered yard will collapse which really would be a bit of a disaster.

## February 10th

He decided to take us for another long walk today. We went down to the river again. He claims He found a primrose flowering on the banks in early February. So what? I'm not mad about water so it's not much fun for me but MF loves it and plunges in and battles with the current. He looks anxious in case His beloved Terrier should be washed away. I notice he doesn't get very anxious if I'm missing for any length of time. He just mumbles "Oh he'll be back soon - he gets agoraphobic and can't bear to be away from me for too long".

That might just be true but rather too complacent to my mind. Anyhow once all the silly fun by the river was finished we had a proper time being horrid to His neighbour's pheasants on the banks. These banks consist of gorse and broom. I managed to hurt my rather too vulnerable feet in a thicket and came out on three legs again. I rather thought I would get some sympathy from Him-sometimes MF licks my wounds but I can't see Him doing that.

One of His most irritating expressions is that "fresh air and exercise will cure it" – that covers more or less every ailment from a head cold to death. I can quite imagine Him saying to someone hovering between this world and the next "pull yourself together man – fresh air and exercise; that's what you need." Anyhow He more or less ignored me so I will have to rely on self help and MF I suppose.

## February 12th

We've still got quite a covering of snow. He calls it malnourished because it's thin, not much of a joke really. He takes us for long walks in the sunshine and my pads are distinctly sore from running on the ice. The farm is, in places, a series of frozen lakes from the recent rains and now He goes off sliding on the ice as if He was a child again. I rather wonder if this is the onset of that well known disease associated with old age – thinking about it I rather doubt it because He's been displaying these symptoms for years.

He's taken to calling my mother "Fuzz Ball" because He says that her hair is more than usually untidy. Pots and black kettles come to mind. Anyhow she goes about the place looking as though someone has shot a few thousand volts through her upholstery. She slides along in the snow doing a snowplough with her nose and then falling over, at which point He kicks snow all over her, which they both seem to enjoy. I regard it as rather ungallant of Him and childish.

## March 8th

Sid's got a whitlow on her finger. It all got very nasty today. At first He took a look at it and thought it just needed lancing and looked out a Stanley knife. Sid looked a bit panic stricken at that but it hurt enough for her to have a try at home surgery. It didn't work of course and she drew the line at His suggestion that He should have a go at it himself as He put it. In the end He thought that maybe she should get a doctor to do whatever they do to whitlows. It's a Saturday so they had to go to Alnwick, some 20 or so miles away, where the only local surgery was open. They did the job there while he browsed in a book shop.

Sid is now all bandaged and says it's all getting better. He was rather relieved to see that it was her left hand so it shouldn't affect her ability to slave too much.

## March 9th

The whitlow is still high on the agenda of conversational topics. Everyone Sid meets gets a blow-by-blow account of the event. He teases her and she reminds Him that when He broke His pelvis He was surrounded by people to fetch and carry and cook and clean not to mention the rest who He coerced into massaging it all better. He points out that a broken pelvis is slightly more fundamental than a poisoned finger. Incidentally it all started when Sid got a splinter from the wooden kitchen table He had had in Dorset and which was the subject of Piglet's little mistake. The implication is that it was His fault for not sterilising the table better. I think it is one of those issues which will take quite a long time to resolve. We just look on in amazement at the triviality of it all. They should try hurting one's foot in the chase.

## November 22nd

He went shooting today dressed in His funny trousers, long socks tied up with string and because it's so cold, a black woollen roll neck shirt under endless layers.
It seems that He was completely incompetent and failed to shoot anything at all. He claims that the organisers played dirty by installing in the beating line the prettiest girl He'd seen for a good few decades. The same girl was next to Him in the line at the snipe bog. He fell headlong over a tussock of reeds while telling her about the time that He went snipe shooting in Ethiopia. What He failed to tell her was that that was in 1956 when her grandparents were young. The other participants watched in amusement tinged with sadness.
Later on in the pub He found out that she was an engineering student at Durham which fascinated Him even more. Anyhow He came back in a dreamy state announcing that once again He was in love. Sid just sighed and got on with preparations for supper. We were pleased to see Him but He hardly noticed us. Poor old chap; He'll recover.

## December 9th

They went to a hunt lunch today. He tidied Himself up by wearing the sports jacket He bought about twenty years ago.

It was a bit on the skimpy side then and in the meantime He hasn't gone down any sizes so He looked a bit like a trussed turkey. A threadbare silk tie didn't do much to elevate the ensemble. His other wife tried right up until the end to smarten Him up a bit but Sid gave up decades ago.

Sid said she hadn't got any money for the tickets so He agreed to finance the expedition. During the inevitable auction He managed to keep His hands in His pockets. However He generously donated a days fishing on the Coquet. It didn't hurt Him much. Sid pays for it. I don't know how He gets away with it?

## April 17th

Well one of the ewes is prolapsing for the second year running but the other three are popping lambs out all over the place. They are mingy little things but their afterbirth is delicious. We try to get to it before the ewe or Sid does.

He is not normally allowed to help on the grounds that sheep are scared of Him. It has been known for Him to kill newborn lambs in ways not heard of before in shepherding circles. He once tried to give one the kiss of life and achieved the technically tricky result of blowing so much air into its tummy that it nearly floated away like a miniature dirigible. It didn't take long to die. On another occasion He had a lamb with lungs full of mucus so He picked it up by its back legs and swung it round in the prescribed manner but it was slippery. At the apex of the swing the lamb slipped out of His hand and hit the wall with a terrific smack thus ending its short life in a dramatic way. So now we understand why He is not normally welcome in the lambing shed and why they went out of proper farming some twenty years ago. It wasn't just sheep that He was a liability with. He managed to Cambridge roll a four acre patch with no rollers attached to the tractor at all. He had left them at the first corner and hadn't noticed. What He had noticed was the family and friends lined up by the garden wall waving at Him trying to point out the error. Needless to say He took their enthusiastic waves to be congratulations on a job well done.

On another occasion He borrowed from their neighbour Geoff a set of flat rollers to roll the hay field. After about two hours Geoff rang up to say that he could hear Him bouncing over the stones from half a mile away and "was He aware that the rollers are water ballasted and needed to be filled up."

## May 10th

We all went fishing on the Coquet with Him and Sid today. The whole thing started with a pantomime laid on by Him. He has bought a fancy set of chest waders. The studded shoes come as a separate item. Well the suit feet are bigger than the shoes so, in his attempt to fit His feet into the shoes, He fell over and was then unable to get up again. Sid pulled Him to His feet. She was trying not to laugh out loud. After a lot of cursing He managed to get both feet into the shoes by which time He was puffed out and had to sit down.

Well He missed the tailgate of the car and sat on the drive. Sid helped Him up again but was no longer able to contain herself and let out a gale of laughter which struck a discordant note with Him. Then came the putting up of the rods. He has a spinner as well as a fly rod. It's the spinner which gets Him rattled. It's all a bit technical. The monofilament started to unravel from the spool as He was trying to feed it through the eyes and it began to fall onto the drive in front of Him. He didn't get cross He just watched bemused it as it continued to unravel itself. Sid came to the rescue. It was at this moment that He decided that he needed a pee! People would pay good money to witness this charade.

We find salmon fishing quite boring because He won't let any of us too close to the river, mainly because it's quite a big bouncy kind of river and he's scared that we will be swept away. I suppose I should be flattered that He cares.

The Coquet is not like the little chalk stream in the South where we still go sometimes and where He does occasionally catch some edible sized fish. Here He hasn't a clue. He has this enormous rod which needs two hands. With his arthritis and frozen right shoulder, caused by the incident on a horse with the hedge in Dorset, He starts at a disadvantage and the fish can relax. In any case with such oversized kit He spends a lot of time retrieving flies and line from huge oak trees that grow near the river. The place is owned by his chum Hugh, who He has dubbed Lord B. He isn't a lord but it amuses Him and everyone else, but is really quite childish. Today the catch was a number of tiny brown trout that would have been regarded as derisory to a child fishing with a jam jar in a stream.

**November 24th**

In theory He is retired but still has a client in the South. It's not such a surprise to find that she is connected with Hollywood and has a nice place in Dorset. He spent a lot of today on the phone to her about her property. He looks smug so we assume He's got it right for once. It seems that He will have to go down there to see her. We usually go with Him because He stays in Worcestershire on the way and He needs us for company. Rather flattering.

His secretary, Margaret, who has a daft dog called Lexy came to see Him this afternoon bringing Lexy with her. In the early days we didn't see eye to eye but we tolerate each other now. Margaret didn't stay long. She had come all the way from Morpeth just to load onto His computer something quite trivial which any half competent seven year old could have done. All He says is that in His early days they had to do mental arithmetic. As if that explains everything.

**December 6th**

Mad Jane has got some allergy or disease. She's covered in spots and can't get her riding hat on because the spots are round her head and neck. Mind you her hair has gone a strange colour so Sid has suggested that maybe it is associated with the dye. I don't think that went down too well because Mad Jane is in the process of courting again and she rather fancied that this change of hue could be the clincher.

Of course this means He has to exercise the Brute. He looks a bit grumpy about it, but at least Jane gets the Brute ready for Him and helps Him on. There's a splendid stone mounting block in the yard but He still seems to need someone to hold the horse as He mounts. Sad really, He should take up something nearer the ground. He hasn't fallen off for a long time which is just as well considering the fuss He makes about getting on. He'd have to find a fork lift truck or walk home leading the Brute.

My mother has had to go into hospital today. It seems she's going to have a mastectomy because she had developed some lumps on her tummy associated with her teats. He had very mixed feelings. His natural instinct was to worry about the implications of the problem in the long term but, as might be imagined, He quite looked forward to the consultation stage. MF is in for the night so heaven knows what that bill will be like and how long it will languish in the unpaid pile beside the phone. From time to time He shuffles the papers and looks anxious but soon recovers when something distracts Him-like the proximity of the whisky bottle.

## December 9th

MF came out of hospital today. She looks completely ridiculous in a bright pink elasticated boob tube. She smells of antibiotics. They were talking about fixing her up with a plastic cone thing to stop her cleaning her wounds, if she could have found them under that stupid bandage arrangement.

He refused point blank to allow her to be put to such undignified discomfort. So there is good in Him. Me and Brain Dead laughed a good deal. MF feels pretty sorry for herself and He fusses over her a lot. I sometimes get the feeling that there is favouritism there but I might be wrong.

## March 19th

Another disaster. Having chucked rat poison tablets into all sorts of places, including the house roof spaces, there is now the most appalling smell of rotting corpses. It is worst in the hall and dining room and futility room. He has been ferreting around in the roof spaces looking for corpses but to no avail. He's getting fussed because His mate Bodget is coming to stay with Mrs Bodget and her sister.

## April 2nd

He's got into a bit of a panic about the dreadful smell and gone out and bought armfuls of flowers to mask the stench. Sid thinks it's great. She's a great flower person; she grows wonderful pelargoniums. So what with all the lilies, stocks and freesias added to the huge pelargoniums the place looks like we're having a wedding. But there is still an underlying smell of corpse!

**April 4th**

The Bodget clan are here. It's good to see them again. Mrs B is good to us and lets us go to sleep on her when she sits down, if Bodget gives her the time to be so relaxed. Bodget hasn't said anything about the smell but keeps going round the house saying "now this is a nice pelargonium – oh! and so is this". All the while He follows him to make sure cuttings aren't being taken too indiscriminately.

After lunch Bodget had to have a little lie down, presumably to recover from the exertions of lusting after Sid's plants and the stress of not being able to pinch any. Mrs Bodget's sister, Angie, and Him took us down to the river for a walk which was a gas. We left Brain Dead at home because He is worried that she might get on the track of a roe deer and either get lost or more probably bump into something while in the chase and need hospitalisation. And we all know how He hates that even if Sid does pay. The river was very low so we could walk across on the slabs of rock where you can see the Roman bridge post holes. I hated that bit because even if the water is thin it still unnerves me having to cross the river at all. The upside is that the other side is good fun with plenty of rabbits and one can imagine all sorts of chaseable things in the grotto.

**May 6th**

We were taken to the nearby pub today to some sort of country fair. There were loads of tents and outside exhibits and dog racing. He, of course thought that we should represent the farm and He entered both MF and me for a terrier race. It is automatically assumed that because my legs are long that I will beat all other comers.

My problem is that when that rabbit takes off I'm determined that none of the other participants are going to get anywhere near it, so a general fight ensues while MF who, by any standards has the most ridiculous little legs, scampered off like an electrified ball of fluff.

After we were all sorted out and with not too much bloodletting, He took us off to look at the Irish dancing which He enjoyed because there were some pretty girls and we sat beside Him licking our wounds. He got chatting to someone who owned a big digger.

Sid looked on with misgivings wondering which bit of the farm was about to be shifted and to where. It really is not too surprising that she has had to resort to medication for her blood pressure. We do feel a bit sorry for her.

## May 8th

Every Thursday we get a pretty mouldy early morning walk and then a long sojourn in the car. He goes to Riding For The Disabled at a livery yard just outside Morpeth. He is not a patient although given the state of His body He could easily qualify. The livery yard is owned by Jane an old hunting friend and she has some friendly dogs of her own. This RDA group is headed up by Samantha who is a Master of the Hunt and she doesn't allow us out to play with Jane's dogs or the children which is a shame. However we get to watch Him. His friend Jim is also a helper so it is no great surprise that the two of them have a whale of a time winding up the dozen or so women helpers. Samantha, keeps a pretty firm grip on the activities however much He and Jim try to undermine the morning's proceedings. When close to horses and their tack He demonstrates total incompetence which Sue, one of the helpers, has noticed so He's not allowed to do anything remotely technical like put the bridle and saddle onto the poor beast. Having been riding for not far off sixty years it's a bit of an indictment of Him and really quite sad. Another of the helpers, Pippa, refers to Him as "Coffin Dodger" which even I think is a bit unfair. Thursdays is also their day fishing on the Coquet so after RDA Him and Sid meet at the river for another wasted day and we get to run riot beside the river. He finds this distracting and uses it as an excuse for never catching anything other than trees and river weed.

## June 17th

Now we know another party is on the horizon. The wine He ordered some days ago arrived today and the "futility" room is once again knee deep in cardboard cases, trays of beer and some token regard for the non-alcoholics. Also this evening a group of tough looking lads arrived in a Land Rover from which emerged a big blue and white tent. He got very excited about it all. The site for the tent is the lawn in front of the house and these lads didn't look too conversant with flower beds (not too many flower beds in the pub!) and He kept telling them to "mind my flowers".

Eventually the boss of the gang politely told Him to go away and in the twinkling of an eye the tent was up. This was great because apart from the two main poles there were heaven knows how many little ones keeping the sides up and suddenly I was provided with an almost endless supply of places to pee.

MF has become blasé about these party preparations and looked at it all with an air of ennui. She could foresee another sleepless night coming up.

Both of His sons are here and potter about looking busy and keeping out of His way for fear that He will suddenly have another impossible idea. "Hurry up James" spent a lot of time playing dreadful music on the Hi-fi machine. He has bought another 100 metres of "fairy lights". The garden is now festooned with these lights as far as the gate into the front paddock where the punters are to park. The old lights from Dorset days are strung all round the tent. They are so old that some of the fittings are bust so they don't work too well. When He switched them on for the first time there was a muted bang and everything went dark. I can't think that it bodes well for the main event whenever that will be.

### June 18th

We used to have four Indian Runner ducks. With the longer evenings Sid and Him go to sleep in front of the telly after their day smartening up the place for this impending event. While they were snoozing Charlie Fox tottered into the yard and removed one duck at a time to feed to her cubs on the moor. It seems that Gregory, in a gallant moment, squared up to the vixen in a vain attempt to protect his wife Peck. That was the end of him. The next night Peck provided the duck supper followed by their dim son who we reckon offered himself as a take-away.

*Me under the barrow*

Eventually Sid got fed up. She awoke to some loud squawking. She legged it into the front yard just in time to witness Charlie exiting stage right so to speak with a mouth full of cockerel this time. Sid, who is known for her powerful voice, yelled at the retreating fox who dropped the battered fowl and took off towards the moor. The cock is now a bit bald but has regained his place in the hen house with remarkable equanimity. The remaining duck, who is now rather poignantly called "Lonely", has taken to living with the hens in their house.

## June 19th

He decided to cut the grass in the front paddock where the cars are to park for the party. Well the ancient Ford tractor hadn't done more than a few circuits before it conked out. Once again the tenacious swallow has nested in it. Now the poor bird has to sit on the nest out in the field which is not at all what she had in mind. He reckons that she rather likes the concept of bringing up her offspring in a mobile home. Anyhow the trusted Mark came to mend it and eventually got it going so He was able to finish the cutting before returning the wretched machine to the shed where the swallows could continue a quieter and more ordered parenthood.

## June 20th

Well it is the day of the party. The rain stopped shortly before the kick off. We were bundled into their bedroom; the rest of the house is groaning under the weight of sons, daughters-in-law and grandchildren all occupying various bedrooms. Even His much loved step-daughter, Geors, is staying with a friend from Ethiopia whose eyes must be out on stalks. She had only been in England three days. He has been made to promise that He won't make any racist remarks – fat chance.

We watched out of the window Him and Nick both wearing wellies disappearing in Sid's car laden with signs to guide the punters to the field. By the time they had put the signs up, punters had begun to arrive so they legged it back to the reception tent to start uncorking the fizz. No one seemed particularly surprised that their host was serving champagne in His wellies. At about the same moment the six piece jazz band began to totter in, weighed down with instruments.

The leader asked Him for some impossibly technical piece of equipment to break the circuits in case the moisture should blow them and their instruments to Kingdom Come – all He could offer were wellies! In the event the band survived.

However the power supply simply couldn't keep pace with all the demands of the spit roast machine, fairy lights and the band so everything blew up eventually. It was all rather reminiscent of His parties in Dorset. One cable began to smoulder so without hesitating He merely plugged it in somewhere else. After a few hours all the fairy lights did explode. Some punters thought it was the cue to go home, so they did.

As a footnote the banjo player was so chilled by the event that he spent the following week in hospital with severe bronchitis. I doubt if they will be coming back. Nothing seems to go entirely to plan when He is involved.

## June 21st

There are a lot of corpses about the place, and more to the point loads of left over lamb and bits. Me and MF went on a scavenging expedition. They were all so bleary eyed they couldn't see us under tables scooping up juicy bits of home-grown sheep and meringues. There were some pretty good cheeses lying around in the dining room. Brain Dead is tall enough to reach them, so she did. I don't think they noticed and anyhow it saved them a lot of hoovering.

This afternoon is the annual inter-village cricket match. You would have thought that they could have organised things a bit better. This year the venue is on the rivals' ground. It turned out to be cunningly concealed by the opposition Captain, Adrian, in an obscure field hidden by a high hedge some distance from his village, thus ensuring that some members of our team never found it, spending a fruitless Sunday afternoon driving round the lanes.

The wicket had been carved out of the middle of a growing field of silage with longish grass as outfield and the boundary marked by electric fence posts in the distance beside the river.
As both teams are largely made up of people who came to the party last night it was a rather uncoordinated and bleary-eyed event.

Our team was half His family including the bewildered girl from Addis Ababa who admitted that she had seen cricket on the television and had been completely mystified by the ritual. Both Geors and Thekdes (The girl in question) were co-opted to play in the absence of a few people, presumably still wandering the lanes looking for the place. He was rather depending on His friend "Alan the Shed" to provide the ringer but he failed to turn up as did the local Judge who gave up the search for the field and went home to sleep the party off. The scorebook seemed to have been misplaced which further delayed things. Thekdes could take neither the cold nor fathom the mysteries of the game. She eventually retired to the makeshift pavilion, a small plastic gazebo, where she put on as many coats and puffa jackets as she could find and tried to hibernate.

The match itself was interesting. Often there was no square leg umpire and when there was he was a member of the batting side but since the sides borrowed players the umpire was often mistaken for a fielder. Thus if a ball went near Him no one moved and the batsmen could run willy-nilly until the situation became clear. Any ball hit off the wicket inevitably stopped dead in the long grass where it became so obscured that it took several fielders to find it, giving the batsmen ample chances to run if they remembered that they should and if they had the energy.

'Hurry up James' and Nick played for both teams. Hurry up James had the distinction of bowling out the last person on his own team thus ensuring victory to the opposition. There were two injuries. One lady umpire was struck smartly on the hip that she had recently had replaced in a Newcastle hospital and her husband broke a finger not catching a ball. Needless to say He claimed that everyone was there at their own risk.

Tea was in Adrian's house.

## June 30th

Sid has decided that Lonely should have some companions. She rang up a friend who lives on a farm out in the wilds and arranged to go there to pick up some ducklings. We were all bundled into the old Mercedes and trundled off there. It really was hillbilly country. At the entrance to the farm is a big pond on which swam a selection of curious looking ducks.

He and Sid went there expecting a couple and returned with a cardboard box full of strange little things with little woolly tam-o'-shanters on their heads. When we got home these little things got put into an improvised cage on the kitchen lawn where we could watch their every move without the privilege of giving them a good run for their money. Why is it that little succulent things like these are so enticing but they loose their allure when they are grown up. One of them looks at you lop-sidedly and falls over if we get too close. I think Charlie will make pretty short work of that one. It is probably another candidate for Sid's healing touch. You can be sure she won't let Him get too close to it.

## July 2nd

Oh dear another catastrophe. The horses were shut into the tiny paddock known as the Pig Pen, not that it has ever contained pigs, in order to avoid contracting laminitis. He had dug a small duck pond there in a wet patch. The now quite grown up Tufted ducks and Lonely have chummed up and go about the place in a gang nattering. Fred, the coloured cob, in a fit of irritation at being shut into a field with no grass took against the ducks and was chasing them round the field. Eventually he managed to kill two. Lonely retired hurt to the duck house where he died and another tufted one has disappeared altogether.

Sid is very upset and has gone off Fred. He is a bit of an oaf but is the equine love of Geors's life having given her some of the best days of her hunting life. He is upset because He really loved those funny ducks with their tufts. There are still three and He says He will get some more.

## July 6th

He's not feeling as perky as usual –the media are full of Swine flu'- the latest must have illness. He thinks He might have it and mopes about the place. He's rather aware that He is getting on a bit and any type of flu' might be fatal and He has too many unfinished projects in mind. A couple of Sid's friends are staying and He finds them thoroughly irritating. The wife crawls out of bed mid morning to eat breakfast and wait around for lunch. The husband has only two topics of conversation: golf, which bores Him to death, and the cruise control on his car. Since His car is still the same Mercedes He's had for many years and has no gadgets except the sunshine roof He has little to say on the subject of cruise control and His views on golf are mostly unrepeatable. He took us on a bit of a yomp across the farm to get away. In view of the energetic nature of the yomp one must surmise that He has probably recovered from swine flu.

## July 10th

Today they took Sid's friends out to the pheasant farm near the coast in His ageing Mercedes. He didn't care much for the comments about how tatty it had become. He regards it as comfortable and much loved: like an old sports jacket. During the journey Sid not only knocked a bit more off the sun visor but almost removed the door handle again. It is now drooping at a funny angle. Moreover when they went over bumps the exhaust pipe hit the ground which He uncharitably put down to the weight of the rear occupants. The husband kept commenting on the fact that the oil light was on. Then the airbag light also came on. The husband announced that his car had seven air bags. It probably didn't go down too well when He joked that that would be handy if one wanted to smother seven people all at the same time. We were confined to the very back because the friends don't seem to like dogs. In a way it was more fun there because we could witness all this covertly. I don't think the husband found His comments very funny.

Now the exhaust was scraping along the road more or less all the time with the added weight of the pheasant feed in the back which gave Him a sort of perverse pleasure.

## July 11th

I don't think my long-sight has ever been too good. Things get a bit blurry in the distance but He rather nigglcd me today. He let out one of His silly laughs when I mistook a mineral bucket in the Pond field for something alien and I stalked it growling. They might have told me. I felt embarrassed. As I say He just laughed in His fanatical way.

Anyhow after that I stuck to objects I could easily identify. One of His pheasants had gone walkabout in West Moor Wood and I chased it into the shrubbery. It made a poor attempt at flying out and garrotted itself on the fence. He rushed to the scene yelling at me and retrieved the corpse. They ate it and though it was a good three months premature they pronounced it delicious. I call that double standards. If they can enjoy eating it why can't I.

## July 13th

Total gloom has descended. He took the beloved Mercedes to his favourite garage near Hexham for a service and MOT today. The mechanic Andy telephoned Him later with the news that the suspension is shot to pieces and that He needed a whole new exhaust system and the bill to get it through its test would be thousands and since the car was only worth a couple of hundred pounds He should scrap it and buy a new car. I must say He gets 10 out of 10 for loyalty. He fought hard but in the end Andy won. After 265,000 miles of very personal and intimate association it probably is time that one of them should retire. The thought of His beloved Mercedes being rendered down into a cube of tin and iron saddened Him a lot. I thought that He might break down but although His upper lip quivered a bit He saw the sense.

The bright piece on this horizon is that the mad government is bribing people to scrap their cars. He says it's lucky they aren't doing the same for husbands because He knew a few who might find themselves on a scrappage scheme! I think that He's on quite thin ice there. He insisted that Sid took a photograph of us in the condemned car for archive purposes.

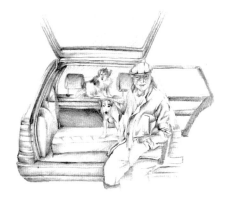

## July 20th

He went to the Audi shop in Newcastle. A silver tongued young salesman didn't take long to sell Him a hugely expensive new estate car. We went with Him and were rather dazzled by the bright shininess of the cars on display. To be honest once He bought one it wouldn't look like that for long. We have never seen Him wash a car yet. Now and then when He simply can't see out or has forgotten what colour it is He puts it through the car wash.

He asked to see a colour chart and was told that he could have black or white. Not a good idea. I should have warned the poor salesman. He went mad. He called the manager over and made Him sit down and lectured Him on the fact that "we'd got past the Model 'T' Ford era sonny" and "how dare they charge such a lot of money for" as He put it "a hearse or a tart's car". Well needless to say He ended up paying for an Anthracite Blue one which looks pretty much black to anyone else.

He refused to have cruise control and Sid said she'd divorce Him again if He had Sat. Nav. He could never get the hang of Sat. Nav. in the helicopter so perhaps it's just as well. He ends up so many blind alleys as it is without electronic aids. It seems that they all have cruise control anyway so He was stuck with that. The salesman was baffled by His refusal to have Sat. Nav. so He had to tell him the story of His friend Gavin whose Sat. Nav. in his Maserati didn't work and how He had irritated the volatile lawyer by looking up their destination on a road map. Every one thought that was very funny for a time except Gavin.

## July 22nd

We had to go back to the Audi shop to pay a deposit. When we got there the silver tongued young man was looking at a very expensive new car which he had tried to drive up a demonstration ramp and had missed so that a good few thousands of pounds worth of car were now in a hedge. All He could find to say was "whoops" which didn't quite catch the mood of the moment.

Another row ensued because although they had now settled on a price which He thought probably represented a good summer holiday for the salesman on commission alone. It seems that to take advantage of the Scrappage Scheme He'd have to present the Mercedes in full colours including a valid MOT. He argued that if a car could pass an MOT it probably shouldn't be scrappable.

He lost the argument. In these circumstances He asked if He could borrow a car – even suggested lending the salesman His bike in exchange for his company car for a couple of months. No deal and this enraged Him. He asked to see another manager who turned out to look as if he should still be in short trousers which made Him even madder.

In the end it transpired that the garage was wrong so they came and collected the corpse with a low loader.

### July 23rd

Today he climbed into a suit, which is not a very frequent event. It seems that it's "Hurry up James's" graduation from Newcastle University. "Hurry Up James" is 35 and has three children and a wife. Once again we got pretty short shrift and they drove off to the university without us. James happens to look quite absurdly young and could easily be mistaken for someone in his early twenties.

He got a first which his father thought was rather letting the side down as everyone else in the family had been content with a 2.2. The ceremony was conducted by Lord Patten who said a few congratulatory words to the clever students who got firsts. Patten assumed that H U James was just another spotty youth so surmised audibly that his parents must be very proud of him. James replied that he hoped that his wife and three children were too. Lord Patton looked a bit thrown by that.

It has to be said that James is a bit unusual and that is all I am prepared to say on the subject.

## July 28th

He decided to take us for a proper walk as He puts it. This means something of a route march down to the river, along it and back past Meldon. In all a distance of about four or five miles. Well poor MF has her annual attack of itchy eyes which comes regular as clockwork. Much of the walk is through long grass and she is lower to the ground than most of us so sadly she bumps into that much more irritating foliage. Anyhow now her face is a swollen mess. It is not an unknown condition. It makes Him laugh when she rubs her eyes on His turn-ups but in reality He knows that her eyes are driving her mad. Last year she had the same affliction so they have all the medication to hand. Needless to say He makes Sid do it because she is "so much better at it". MF is very good at taking her medication. I fight like hell. She lies on her back with her feet in the air and positively basks in the attention. I would have savaged the lot of them.

## August 18th

He's down in Worcestershire again. He rang in today to say that all the electrics in the cottage had gone. It didn't matter what He did the trip switch kept tripping. As if poor Sid could do something about it from 300 miles away. There was a long moan about no Aga to cook on and no light or television. He had to force Himself to go to the pub at Knightwick for His supper and some beer. What sacrifices these arty types make. He couldn't write of course because it was all too dark in the house. I suppose He just wanted to let off steam. He had taken MF with him. So at least He had company. She doesn't seem to mind cold and dark. At the farm she sleeps day in day out wrapped up in an old duvet in the inhospitable futility room. It is rumoured that They are going to install a wood burning stove in there so she will have to find somewhere else that is cold and damp; maybe the dining room would fit the bill.

Apparently He and MF went to bed at 9.00 p.m. with four candles so that he could read His book instead of which he fell asleep listening to His beloved Radio 4 extra. It repeats all the nostalgic programmes that he heard first time round when He was just a lad. It surprises me that they had wireless in those days.

**August 19th**

Well He's been on the phone again. It seems that in His usual brash way He has trolled round a few locals until He found a man who is an 80 year old retired builder and dragged the poor man into the house to find the electrical fault. MF said that it was like one of His pantomimes again. They went into the loft where they found a pipe leaking onto some electrics. After a time Geoff decided to isolate a bit of water pipe which meant stopping the flow or something. After a lot of banging and bad language there was a clatter and water cascaded through the bathroom ceiling and thence down into the cloakroom finally swamping the kitchen. All this while Geoff was yelling at Him to turn off the stop cock outside. In the meantime part of the bathroom ceiling fell down. He finally found the stop cock in the garden and returned to the loft. By this time Geoff was brewing up for a coronary and had gone a funny colour.

According to MF it was one of the best shows He had ever put on. Geoff is still alive but contrives to be out if He happens to walk past his house. I expect that as soon as the locals see His car in the drive the word goes out.

**August 21st**

Whoops! Whenever they hatch out chicken eggs, almost all of them turn out to be cockerels but this time there were two hens. Sid locked up the two new hens with the other rag tag and bobtail bunch in the henhouse for forty-eight hours for integration purposes. Well today He let them out. The two poults being unfamiliar with the topography went tottering off into the pond field which is on our morning ritual walk route. MF and I found the chicks messing about amongst the creeping thistles down near the pond. I marked the brown one while MF got the black one. He was apoplectic rushing about flailing, ineffectually with a lead. MF dropped hers on the grounds that she can't run that fast anymore but I legged it, face full of young chicken, through the stables to the pole barn with Him bellowing in the background. Eventually I got a fit of conscience and I have to say He's pretty accurate with a lead (all that hunting whip practice I expect) so I dropped it beside His lorry and tail down I crept back into the house – He got me as I went through the door. It didn't hurt much. MF has gone to ground in the crockery cupboard in the futility.

Sid is now patching up the brown poult, which has a broken wing and a few minor blemishes. It now has a powder blue boob tube on and sits in a cardboard box beside the aga.

## August 22nd

When Sid's mother died Sid inherited her huge white cat called Snowy. It was soon renamed Avalanche. Quite early on it defected to the Granny wing where cats are more tolerated and where they don't run the gauntlet of our teeth. Avalanche isn't very well. They all agree that if he isn't better by Monday Sid will take Him to the vet along with the chicken if it doesn't stop toppling over.

## August 23rd

He took us for one of His more energetic walks again; this time into Codlaw Wood. From there we do a biggish detour round Old Park and then back to the farm over the moor. Sasha went off on one of her hoolies after not much I expect. She returned on three legs. She's hobbling about and Sid has gone all soppy with her on the sofa in the sitting room. MF's weepy eyes syndrome has returned and she is always rubbing them on His trouser turn-ups. He of course puts it all down to affection. What an ego! So Sid has decided to make a block booking at the vet for Monday to include two dogs, a cat and the chicken.

## August 24th

What a weird lot tumbled out of Sid's car at the surgery. He had sat with the chicken in a cardboard box on His knees and the rest of us in the back. Me and MF had to be confined in the far back so that we couldn't further distress Avalanche in his plastic cat basket and the chicken well out of our reach. Sasha had to have an x-ray as did Avalanche, and it turns out, surprise, surprise, that Sasha had only a minor sprain, but poor Avalanche had to go to the mouse hunting ground in the sky. He's going to be buried in one of the woods on the farm.

*Another tiring day*

The chicken looks very silly in a new boob tube applied by the vet and the irony is that it is a green one with little dog paw prints for decoration. I think Sid reckons that it is a sick joke dreamt up by Him and the vet.

There was an expedition for all of us over to the wood with Avalanche for the burial ceremony. As might be expected He made a fuss about the difficulty of digging because of the tree roots. In fairness, given the size of the deceased, the hole had to be pretty big.

**October 10th**

They went to his aunt's funeral today. It's amazing to think that there is anyone of a generation before Him who could possibly still be alive. She died in Essex so they went by plane and he hired a big black car which He hated saying that He now knew what it was like to be Mondeo Man. He considered that at least the colour was appropriate.

They were early for the service so He took Sid into an enormous supermarket where He found a really cheap bottle of whisky. Sid told Him that as they had only hand luggage He would have difficulty getting it back to Northumberland but He knew better, of course. " It's an internal flight they don't worry about that sort of thing." He said.

After a pretty dismal service and wake which seemed to be full of ageing relatives eyeing up the next victim He and Sid headed off to the airport. Sure enough His bottle was not allowed in the cabin. Neither would they allow it in the hold with just a label round its neck as He suggested. He refused to leave it behind. So He had to buy a natty little £30 rucksack for it and some bubble wrap. This was then presented at check-in. But because it contained a bottle it had to go into the hold. He had to join another queue and pay another fee of £16. By this time He was getting visibly irritated but such is His nature He wasn't going to be beaten so He paid up and watched His now £60 bottle of whisky disappear into the bowels of Stansted Airport. He said that He had never paid that much for a bottle of anything before so He was going to savour every sip.

All in all an expensive send off to dear old Veronica who right up to just a few days before she died referred to Him by her pet name of "Scallywag".

# December 10th

He doesn't often get cross, sailing through life on a wave of optimism and whisky, but He got mad today. Having waited three months for the delivery of His new car they rang up on this the day of delivery to say that they had ordered the wrong car! It was a very nice car but not the one He had ordered. It didn't have a sunshine roof which was the only extra that he wanted without which He regarded it as utterly useless. He gave Gareth and his boss at the Audi shop in Newcastle quite a hard time. He did a deal which took some of the sting out of the situation and Gareth delivered the car at just about "Top off bottle" time. Gareth and his driver came in for a snifter but as it was a Friday night they wanted to get off home quickly so He let them off the hook and bafflingly gave them a bottle of wine each.

Needless to say He wanted to move the wretched thing from the drive to the barn but had sent Gareth home without getting any instructions. It hadn't occurred to Him that during the fifteen years that had elapsed since He bought the Mercedes motor technology had moved along a bit.

He wasn't ready for the fact that just going through the process of unlocking the thing with a remote key caused it to light up like a Christmas tree. Apparently it also needed more than putting the key into the hole and turning it to start it. However at this moment two screens lit up and the radio came on playing a nifty little tune from Metro Radio. He winced at the sound effects and it didn't occur to Him to look at either of the screens. He imagined they were there for decoration. In any case ordinary broadcast television sends Him to sleep pretty well instantly so two screens in His car is a recipe for disaster.

After several visits back to the kitchen with the instruction manual which ran to two volumes, one dealing exclusively with the sound system and both of them completely incomprehensible He returned to the car having discovered how to start it. He was now equipped with a rather dim torch to see if He could find the hand brake which the manufacturers had hidden. To His amazement there wasn't one-how can you make a car without a hand brake-madness. Of course if He had considered for a moment the psyche of the German who designed the beast He would have realised that they had accounted for daft old codgers like Him and one of the screens actually gave clear and brief instructions as to how to mobilise the beast.

Indeed it even tells you what gear you are in and which one Fritz reckons you should be in. Anyhow after a longish interval He managed to get the thing going and put away in the barn. There was the very slight inkling that He wasn't going to like this car.

## December 12th

Having said that He doesn't often get cross He has done it again. In fairness to Him I think He had good cause again and it's just coincidence that it has happened twice in a month.

He has spent months rearing a few pheasants for the "Boys" to shoot at and goes round almost every day feeding the wretched birds. He has even hit on a magic mixture which seems to attract some of His neighbour's partridges. A really healthy gang of birds were now established in the woods and He proudly announced the numbers every time He returned from a feeding expedition. What's more He doesn't allow us into the woods for fear that we will disturb His beloved birds. He's right.

Well his neighbours were holding one of their very formal and grand shooting days with rich Tyneside businessmen and a fleet of Range Rovers appeared in the field adjacent to His main wood. He was standing watching with awe the clouds of pheasants and partridges filling the skies ahead of the beaters. His admiration turned to anger when suddenly about five gundogs erupted from one of His woods. At the same moment a cloud of His pheasants star-burst over His head going in all directions.

He started yelling at the dogs which took not a blind bit of notice. Then He headed up the wood which was, of course, now empty of pheasants but knee deep in Spaniels and Labradors. As He went so his yelling got louder and louder. Eventually He caught up with the hapless beater who owned some of the dogs.

There was a bit of surreptitious scuttling into Range Rovers in the background and the beaters shuffled off leaving Him to sit on a hunt jump quietly having a stroke. Someone later told Him that those were the precise circumstances in which men of His age have heart attacks. His reply was that they might have taken a bit more notice of Him in those circumstances mightn't they.

## December 13th

He went to see the very nice gamekeeper for the neighbouring shoot today. Dennis apologised for the excitement yesterday and between them they worked out a formula that would work. The shoot is run by His friend Hugo so really all was forgiven pretty quickly. Hugo is trying to find Him a nice old Land Rover for the farm for not too much money. As if He hasn't got enough vehicles.

We found a dead rabbit in West Moor Wood. It was wonderfully rank. My Mother and I had a tug of war over it. Eventually it separated. She got the body and I got the head. He got pretty agitated and tried to relieve both of us of whatever bit was still in evidence though MF, being used to His spoil sport ways had ingested quite a lot by the time He got to her. He is just a bit wary of my pointy teeth so He left me to crunch my way through the head as we made our way home. He found that mildly amusing and smiled. I see what my Mother means about that smile. It is a bit unnerving. It seemed to amuse Him that the rabbit's ears seemed to go in whole so to speak.

## December 15th

MF's bit of the rabbit came back up all over the kitchen floor last night. Sid is good the way she copes with our indiscretions. He looks painfully at the mess and skirts round it pretending that some pressing matter in the stables needs His immediate attention. He does

*Me sleeping in a cat's bed*

take us for some good walks and today was no exception but because of MF's kitchen excitement He took a lot of notice of her movements if you get my drift. It's quite personal in my opinion.

Incidentally the little brown hen that I took for a walk round the yard and buildings is now fully operational again and indeed is the only hen to be laying what are admittedly rather small eggs. There! It just goes to show that to get them to buck up their egg laying ideas you need a terrier in charge.

## January 6th

We like Thursdays, me and the gang. Jimmy the Meat visits in his rickety yellow van from which he sells wonderful meat straight from the Cheviot hills. The people in the cottage are vegetarians so it seems all wrong that Bobby their mad Italian dog always gets a bone whereas we, who come from an aggressively red-meat family, only get them now and then.

Anyhow disaster has struck because it seems that Jimmy is giving up. Sid thinks he may have fallen out with the boss. They do have differences of opinion about meat now and then and on those occasions, when he visits the farm, he and Sid get to chewing the fat, metaphorically speaking, and Jimmy's visit lasts for ever.

## January 10th

Last night there were strange goings on outside. He had just about gone to bed. Sid is convinced that He thinks He will turn into a pumpkin if He stays up after 10pm but even He heard the fire engine and saw all the flashing lights. He was strangely unconcerned but took the trouble to look out of a window to check that nothing hereabouts was on fire.

It turns out that the Cottage people saw a fire in the distance with sparks and everything so they rang the fire station. It seems that there was nothing interesting and everything went quiet again and He nodded off with His book on His chest and His glasses at a crazy angle on His nose.

He quizzed Sid this morning about the excitement. It is coincidental that Jimmy the Meat is a part time fireman and he and the rest of the fire engine crew had come in for a chat after the excitement last night and He had slept through it all. All He could say was that whatever they were on down at the cottage He would like some.

## January 12th

Today was the second and last shoot of the winter on this farm. He asked His friend David together with his son Richard to help look for the hapless pheasants. David brought both his gun dogs which was rather ambitious of him. So what with Jim's two, Bryans two and David's the pheasants were kept on the move a good bit and the guns outnumbered by dogs.

In the event the bag was a bit unexpected. Certainly they managed to shoot more pheasants than ever before but the bag was enhanced by the addition of two chickens including Arthur Bumfluff the magnificent new cock who was just learning to strut his stuff. It seems that the shooters were so excited by the number of birds shot that they didn't notice David's Springer augmenting the bag in this unusual way. No one seemed particularly bothered by it.

## May 8th

Mad Jane's friend Nicki has a boyfriend called Brick. He is very keen on water fowl. He turned up today with nine ducks. They are temporarily in a sheep pen with a huge orange plastic bowl for a pond. When they settled down they all decided to go for a swim at the same time thereby displacing more or less all the water. He nearly had a fit. He could see that he could spend the rest of His life filling the bowl. Me and MF took to chasing the daft things up and down the pen but that got quite boring and He went a funny colour trying to stop us.

They've got the old collie kennel in the pig pen so He has decided to do some of His "temporary" fencing. He's got Sid out there to hold onto fence posts which she does with obvious terror while He swings a fence post basher about in a thoroughly dangerous way. Not one fence post ended up vertical but at least he didn't maim Sid. Then the netting went on in a sort of scalloped way and the gate is a tatty sheep hurdle wound on with wire to one of the leaning posts. Once they had done that they started to try to catch the brutes and put them into their new house. He managed to lose one completely. It legged it off into the buildings and became invisible. It didn't seem to worry Him much. The tenants came out to watch the fun so He set them onto trying to find the runaway duck.

**May 9th**

The missing duck is back. He found it pottering about the yard looking for water and its friends presumably. All the ducks are looking slightly bewildered in their new house and making a frightful noise. We really can chase them now because they don't have anywhere to hide. He bellows as usual and we slink off to the Strip Wood to annoy the resistant hen pheasant who helps herself to chicken food in the sheds.

Me and MF had such a laugh this morning. We went on our customary walk to the big wood and on the way back, as usual, He put me on a lead to stop me going off to beat up Bobby. Well If I shake my head the noose goes loose and at that point I can reverse out of it. If He's not concentrating, which if the truth is known is more or less all the time, He doesn't notice. Anyhow today He ambled back to the farm apparently taking a dog lead for a walk. Me and Fish pottered unhindered past Him. As we approached the muck heap he twigged that I was no longer attached to Him. I think He felt a bit foolish because He didn't say anything.

**June 17th**

Our next door farmer, Geoff, has had a dreadful road accident on his quad bike. It was just about the time that He went to his usual Thursday job in Morpeth helping at RDA. When he got to Geoff's farm there was Geoff sprinkled over the road with the air ambulance on his lawn and police and paramedics all over the place. Actually to give Him his due He was visibly shaken by it. They've known Geoff for more than thirty years.

**July 1st**

He and Sid went to see Geoff in Hospital. He made the typically tacky comment that He reckoned Geoff had done it on purpose to avoid having to go to the village fete on the Sunday. He also reckoned that Geoff was showing off by having a helicopter on his lawn. Geoff thought this was quite funny which was good of him considering he was nearly killed. There was a bit of banter about posh people and helicopters on lawns so Geoff told them about the time that he had had a pair of special boots delivered to him some years ago by Chinook piloted by a friend in the RAF. His chum had flown low over the farmhouse and chucked them out of the helicopter.

During the conversation in hospital they touched on the matter of the ducks. It seems that their friend Brick kept his ducks on Geoff's farm. Amongst the nine that Brick had delivered to Him and Sid was a white tufted one. Guess what it was the one which had done a runner during the Fred episode back in May. Apparently it had walked the half mile or so to Geoff's farm to avoid the inherent dangers of this farm. It can't have been too pleased to have been unceremoniously shipped back again.

*Mum and me by the Aga*

## July 15th

Disaster has struck our world. He has injured His knee and He can no longer walk very far with us. He's been to two doctors, countless physiotherapists and a knee specialist none of whom has cured Him. He rather unadvisedly wrote to the Telegraph about it all sparking a discussion on the relative merits of doctors and vets in which vets definitely came out on top. He rather unadvisedly sent His GP a copy of the correspondence thinking that it would amuse him. At that point His doctor fell out with Him.

No one knows when, if ever, He will be well enough to continue His overactive lifestyle. He has even had to stop riding the brute horse but as His friend Romy said not long ago "It's time some people knew when to retire." She said this with her gimlet eyes firmly looking at Him.

## July 20th

Today is the saddest day of my life. MF has been ill all this week. Normally she is pretty good at the trough but she stopped eating almost a week ago. The vet tried all sorts of things but in the end the X-ray showed some sort of major problem in her giblets which was irreparable. I know how much He loved her but having to put her to sleep was the only option. He was visibly shaken by it. A real cloud has descended on the whole place.

He and Sid took her down to the wood where she is now buried. He had to get the chain saw out to get through some tree roots so she had the last laugh. Sid has planted some primroses on the grave and we troop past each day and He is soppy. I will miss her to bits.

**END**

**☙ The ☙**
# JOURNAL
**☙ of ☙**
# MORTIMER
# FISH

The Adventures and Mishaps
of a Jack Russell terrier.
As told in her own words
to Him.

The adventures and mishaps of a Jack Russell terrier. As told in
her own words to Him.
Beautifully illustrated with line drawings, this book records
real incidents in the early life of Mortimer Fish and her elderly
canine companions Comatose and Bugger Off.

Available from Powdene Publicity - £7.95 (plus £1 p&p)
Tel. 0191 265 0040. email:info@powdene.com